The

Bumblebees

of Kent

By Nikki Gammans and Geoff Allen

Published by the Kent Field Club

Published by Kent Field Club, the Natural History Society of Kent

The aims of the Kent Field Club are to promote an increased interest in natural history, to study and record the distribution and ecology of fauna and flora, and to promote nature conservation in association with the relevant organisations within the County of Kent.

First published 2014

ISBN 978-0-9561926-5-3

Cover design: Simon Daverin
Front cover photograph: ♀ *Bombus hortorum* © Alan Kenworthy
Back cover photograph: ♀ *Bombus subterraneus* © John Oates
The Kent Field Club and the Authors thank Dr Paul Williams and the Authorities of the Natural History Museum, London (NHM) for permission to use photographs of pinned bumblebees from their collections, taken by Nick Withers.

CONTENTS

THE BUMBLEBEES OF KENT
by Nikki Gammans & Geoff Allen

INTRODUCTION

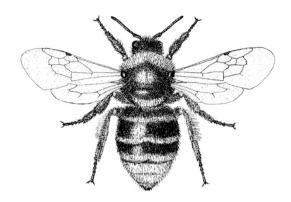

♀ *Bombus subterraneus*
Short-haired bumblebee © Geoff Allen

About this book

The bumblebees (genus *Bombus*), with their economic importance, aesthetic value, declining numbers and fascinating social lifecycles, are worthy of a more comprehensive treatment than that given in Allen (2009) and this is provided here, with updated maps and more extensive species profiles.

This book discusses the importance of bumblebees, their declines and how we can help to reverse those declines. It also contains detailed descriptions of bumblebee ecology, anatomy and their Kent distribution, followed by descriptions of each bumblebee species present in Kent. The book aims to provide a comprehensive guide to bumblebee ecology.

The authors

Nikki Gammans graduated in Biology and Ecology at the University of

Edinburgh. She was then awarded a Ph.D in ant ecology from the University of Southampton and The Centre for Ecology and Hydrology. Having completed her Ph.D, she went to the United States to do a one year post doctoral diploma in invasive ant species. She led a Species Recovery Programme for the critically endangered Red-barbed ant *Formica rufibarbis* in Surrey before transferring to bumblebees and becoming the Project Officer for another Species Recovery Programme, the Short-haired Bumblebee *(Bombus subterraneus)* Project.

Geoff Allen was fascinated by the social insects from a very young age and studied them seriously from his mid-teenage years. He now has some 45 years experience in this field and is the Kent Recorder for the aculeates (bees, stinging wasps and ants). He wrote the book *Bees, Wasps and Ants of Kent* which was published in 2009 and now spends some of his time volunteering for the Short-haired Bumblebee Project.

The authors near Malmö, Skåne, in southern Sweden, 2013
© Gill Williams

CHAPTER 1
ABOUT BUMBLEBEES

Evolution of the bees
Introducing the Hymenoptera
The bees are placed in the vast insect order Hymenoptera, advanced insects which have two pairs of membranous wings, the fore pair of which are larger than the hind pair. Each hind wing is linked to the corresponding fore wing when the insect is in flight, the connection being made by a row of small hooks on the front edge of the hind wing which link onto a fold in the hind edge of the fore wing.

The basic division of the Hymenoptera is into two suborders on the basis of the lack of (Symphyta) or presence of (Apocrita) the wasp waist. Older classifications were based more on the structure of the ovipositor but this is subject to enormous variations across the order, resulting in more suborders formerly being recognised. Symphyta includes the sawflies, woodwasps and their relatives, whilst Apocrita constitutes the remainder, including groups such as the gall wasps, chalcids, ichneumons, braconids and the aculeates (from *aculeus* – Latin, a sting), i.e. the bees, stinging wasps and ants.

The aculeates are a section or series within the suborder Apocrita. Both ants and bees are believed to have evolved from aculeate wasps, although from different groups. The ants, which lost their wings except in the reproductives, so becoming terrestrial, and the change of the bees' larval diet to vegetarian (i.e. pollen), enabled the aculeates to diversify considerably. The bees are a large, diverse but closely related, group found world-wide.

Behaviour
The bees are believed to have evolved from solitary wasps placed in the modern family Crabronidae. The constricted waist, so useful to wasps when paralysing prey (making the abdomen, or more strictly, the gaster,

very mobile for deployment of the sting), has been retained by the bees and gives structural evidence for their origin. The ancestral bee, rather than hunting insects, began to use pollen to feed its larvae. This could have originated from the adult pre-bee's habit of feeding on nectar from flowers and finding the pollen very nutritious. A dearth of insect prey might have precipitated the behaviour. A radiation of diversity saw the bees and angiosperms (flowering plants) co-evolve to the situation we have today, where there are many specialisations on the part of both bees and flowers for this life way. The sting, originally a tool for hunting, became used solely for defence.

The group of bees with pollen baskets on the hind legs (the corbiculate bees) seem particularly pre-adapted to form eusocial colonies. The bumblebees (genus *Bombus*), stingless bees (Meliponini) and honeybees (genus *Apis*) all form colonies where there is a reproductive division of labour in the females, with a queen laying the eggs and the workers carrying out all other tasks. The males appear only for a short time in the colony cycle and their sole function is to mate with potential queens, after which they soon die.

The fossil record

The most primitive Hymenoptera, related to the modern sawflies, first appeared in the fossil record in the Triassic period of the Mesozoic era. These insects, like their modern relatives, lack the wasp waist, which probably did not appear until the middle Jurassic. The first primitive aculeates appeared in the fossil record in the late Jurassic. The adaptive radiation beginning at the very start of the Cretaceous period (Berriasian epoch) saw the formation of many of the modern families of Hymenoptera. The early "apoid" wasps (i.e. wasps placed in the superfamily Apoidea as relatives of the bees) first appeared at this time. The bees may have originated in the Barremian or Aptian epochs (125 Mya: millions of years ago) of the Lower Cretaceous. An earlier origin (135-130 Mya) in the Hauterivian epoch is less likely.

CHAPTER 1 ABOUT BUMBLEBEES

The oldest known bee is an amber fossil *Melittosphex burmensis* from the Albian or Cenomanian epochs of the Lower Cretaceous of Myanmar, about 100 Mya. It shows a combination of many bee and wasp characteristics analogous to the most primitive ant fossil, *Sphecomyrma freyi*, also of the same age, which combines wasp and ant characteristics. *Melittosphex* is regarded by some as a bee not on the main line of evolution but by others, as a pemphredonine wasp (Crabronidae) synonymous with the extinct genus *Cretospilomena* from the same deposits.

The corbiculate bees are thought to have originated some 80-90 Mya and the oldest known member of this lineage is a stingless bee *Cretotrigona prisca* (originally described as *Trigona prisca*). *Cretotrigona prisca* is an amber fossil from New Jersey, originally believed to be from 80 Mya but now dated at 65 Mya, close to the Cretaceous-Tertiary boundary. It is placed in the highly evolved eusocial bee group, Meliponini and is very similar to extant forms.

When one comes to search for fossil bumblebees, there is a lack of reliable *Bombus* material before the Miocene epoch of the Tertiary period but their origin is thought to have been as early as the Eocene epoch. Some of the Eocene genera from Baltic amber represent three extinct lines of corbiculate bees. They show various combinations of characters which make them separate from but intermediate between bumblebees, stingless bees and honeybees. True stingless bees are also present in this amber but not bumblebees or honeybees. The honeybee genus *Apis* itself is unknown before the early Oligocene.

Three types of bee

The bees are characterised as a group by the females' habit of collecting pollen from flowers to feed the larvae in a nest they have constructed (although two unrelated groups of wasps do the same). They usually have hairy bodies and legs to collect and carry the pollen back to the nest, separating them from the wasps. The nest types and life cycles of the bees are many and varied, but the UK species can be broadly divided into three different types: the solitary bees, the bumblebees and the honeybee.

The solitary bees show much diversity, with some 230 species in Britain.

♀ *Andrena thoracica* — a solitary bee
© Geoff Allen

♂ *Heriades truncorum* — a solitary bee
© Geoff Allen

Their ranks contain such groups as the mining bees, the mason and leafcutter bees, the long-horned bees and the carpenter bees. They are similar in having a simple life cycle in which each female bee makes her own nest. (However, some mining bee species in *Halictus* and *Lasioglossum* are primitively eusocial). After mating, the female solitarily founds her nest, constructs the first cell, provisions it with a pollen and nectar mix, and then lays an egg into the cell. It is then sealed. The next cell is then constructed, provisioned and sealed, and so on. The hatching larvae feed on the stored pollen-nectar mix until it is gone and then each pupates in its cell, usually emerging as an adult in the following year. A female may sequentially construct more than one nest. Each female provisions only her own nests and a colonies of individuals are never formed.

When most people hear bees mentioned, they think of beehives, bee-keepers and produce like honey, royal jelly and beeswax. There is in fact only one species of bee kept in hives in Britain by beekeepers, the Western honeybee *Apis mellifera*. This bee lives in complex perennial societies, constructing the marvellously engineered wax combs of hexagonal cells used for brood rearing and storing honey. The females are divided into two castes, the queen and her many daughter workers. There is only one queen per colony and she is structurally and behaviourally different from the worker caste, lacking pollen baskets and the instinct to forage. She spends all her time during the active period of the colony laying eggs and this is her one allotted task in the life cycle. The workers carry out all other duties, from cleaning cells in the brood comb and feeding the larvae, to defending the nest or hive from intruders and to foraging for food for their nest mates and the larvae. During the winter, each colony, queen and workers, survives in a cluster in the hive, feeding on stored honey. Colony reproduction is by swarming, sometimes called colony fission. Here the old, incumbent queen leaves the hive with a proportion of the workers to set up a new nest. A new queen is reared in the old hive from queen brood already existing for the purpose. After this queen emerges as an adult, she goes on a mating flight, pairing with several males (drones). She only mates at this one time in her life, before settling down in her hive to become little more than an egg-laying machine. Drones are present in the hives only during the swarming season, which is May to July in Britain; after this

Worker *Apis mellifera* — the honeybee
© Geoff Allen

they are unceremoniously thrown out of the hives to die.

The bumblebees (genus *Bombus*), with 21 social species recorded from Britain, are a halfway house between these two types of life way. There

is a phase where the queen solitarily founds her nest and then a longer eusocial phase, from the emergence of the first workers until the end of the colony cycle, when males and then the new queens are reared. Because she has to carry out all of the tasks her workers will do when they emerge, the queen has not lost the ability to forage for pollen and nectar. She has pollen baskets and

♀ *Bombus pascuorum* — a carder bumble-bee © Geoff Allen

a honey crop in similar fashion to the workers. The latter are in fact just like small versions of their mother queen but are unmated, with undeveloped ovaries (however under certain circumstances they can lay male-determined eggs, see Chapter 1: Colony structure and foraging).

The world distribution of bumblebees

The bumblebees are believed to have originated in the Tibetan region some 34 Mya (millions of years ago), in response to a cooling event in the world's climate during the late Eocene epoch. The most dramatic uplifting of the Himalayas and Tibetan plateau did not take place until about 21 Mya, when the bumblebees diversified in the new cold conditions. With their dense coat of insulating hair, they could control their temperature to a considerable extent. This was achieved by vibrating the wing muscles which had the effect of raising the thoracic temperature above that of the surroundings. They could therefore fly at lower temperatures and had a selective advantage over other less hirsute bees without this behavioural specialisation. It is in Himalaya where the greatest diversity of subgenera and species is still found (Williams, 1991).

The dense coat of hairs possessed by the bumblebees meant that they could not penetrate far south into the lowland Indian subcontinent with its tropical climate, as they would overheat in such conditions. They exist only in montane regions there. There was also competition from several species of honeybee and the many stingless bees in the Indian subcontinent. However, they radiated out of their ancestral home into the Old World temperate regions (the Palaearctic region) and then to those of the New World (the Nearctic region). *Bombus* reaches right into the Arctic Circle in both the Old and New Worlds.

A small group of *Bombus* species that were more adapted to warmth, colonised the New World tropics (the Neotropical region), even including one or two species in the Amazon valley. Most South American species are found in the Andean countries, however, and one has reached Tierre del Fuego. This colonisation may have been aided by a lack of competition because there are no species of honeybee native to the New World, although stingless bees are found in the New World tropics.

There are no native *Bombus* found in Africa south of the Sahara (the Afrotropical region). This could be due to competition from honeybees and stingless bees. However, bumblebees have penetrated into the Oriental region, including some at lower elevations, and beyond to some of the oceanic islands, but not as far as Australasia.

Some bumblebees have been introduced into non-indigenous areas by deliberate human agency, to help with pollination. Thus in late Victorian times, queens of four British *Bombus* species, the Garden bumblebee *B. hortorum*, the Ruderal bumblebee *B. ruderatus*, the Short-haired bumblebee *B. subterraneus* and the Buff-tailed bumblebee *B. terrestris* were taken to New Zealand to pollinate the introduced red clover which is used for cattle fodder. The few indigenous New Zealand bees were not useful to cattle farmers in this respect. The first three of these *Bombus* are very effective for red clover pollination, the last not quite so. However, *B. terrestris* is one of the best pollinators of tomatoes, with its "buzz pollination" (sonication) behaviour. It has appeared in Tasmania to the delight of tomato growers (but not ecologists) and may reach mainland Australia. *B. ruderatus* was also taken to Chile for red clover pollination. It has spread into neighbouring provinces of Argentina, and was recently but inadvertently described as a new species from Chile!

Quarantine should always be used when transporting *Bombus* queens, to prevent the cross infection of indigenous bumblebee species. Transportation for the tomato pollination industry in the United States is likely to have been the cause of the decimation of some *Bombus* species, by infection from queens carrying aggressive parasitic microorganisms.

The Kent species

The British list has 27 species of bumblebee, including 21 social species (queen and worker caste) and six cuckoos (parasites of social colonies). Of the former, three are extinct in the UK, these being the Apple bumblebee *Bombus pomorum*, Cullum's bumblebee *B. cullumanus* and the Short-haired bumblebee *B. subterraneus*. The first of these, recorded only from Kent, may never have been truly British; it may have been a colonising species which never became established. The other two were British and found in Kent. *B. subterraneus* is the subject of a Species Recovery Programme, the Short-haired bumblebee project. Also extinct in Kent is the Great yellow bumblebee *Bombus distinguendus*, which has retreated northwards to the north of Scotland, some of the Western Isles and the Orkneys. Kent is the most important county in the UK for bumblebee diversity, having six of the seven UK BAP (Biodiversity Action

Plan) schedule 41 species. There are currently 22 species of bumblebee recorded in Kent.

Two forms of White-tailed bumblebee, *B. magnus* and *B. cryptarum*, are so similar to *B. lucorum* that they have only recently been recognised as distinct species. Only the queens can satisfactorily be identified without recourse to molecular analysis. *B. magnus* is common in the South-west, Wales and the North but is not an upland species. There is only one known Kent specimen. *B. cryptarum* has not yet been conclusively recorded from Kent.

The Blaeberry or Bilberry bumblebee *B. monticola* is a rare upland species found in the hills of the South-west, Wales and the North, and is not found in Kent.

The Tree bumblebee *Bombus hypnorum* is a recent colonist to Britain, first recorded in the UK in 2001 near Southampton and from Kent in 2006. It has since rapidly spread across the country and become one of the "Big 7" common species. One reason for its success is its unique habit of nesting in hollows in tree trunks previously used by nesting birds. It readily adapts to tit nesting boxes. The queens are known to be very opportunistic. Thus it has no competition in nesting sites from other bumblebees and bucked the trend of decline in other species.

THE BUMBLEBEES OF KENT

Ecology
Lifecycle of bumblebees

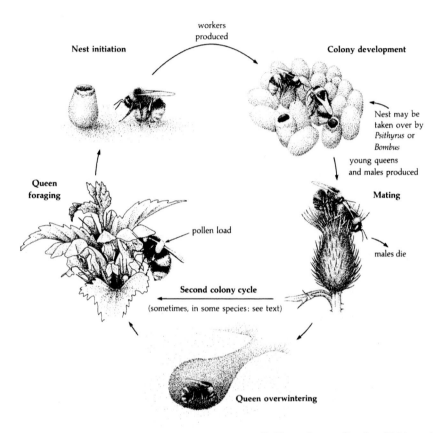

workers produced

Nest initiation

Colony development

Nest may be taken over by *Psithyrus* or *Bombus*

young queens and males produced

Queen foraging

Mating

pollen load

males die

Second colony cycle

(sometimes, in some species: see text)

Queen overwintering

Psithyrus is now *Bombus (Psithyrus)*
© Tony Hopkins. From Prŷs-Jones and Corbet (2011)

Nesting ecology, building and location
Compared with other social insects, bumblebee colonies are very short-lived and do not survive from year to year. A queen bumblebee emerges

from hibernation to found and form a colony. Our bumblebee species are divided into early and late emergers. The early emergers appear from January-March/April and the late ones from May onwards. The earliest queens to be seen, some even before the turn of the year, may not have even entered hibernation from a late nest the previous year, and are of the Buff-tailed bumblebee *Bombus terrestris*. The Tree bumblebee *B. hypnorum* may also be seen early in the year. Queens hibernate in north facing aspects so they are not roused by the sun too early in the year and nest in south/south-east facing aspects to absorb the warmth from the morning sun.

When a queen emerges from hibernation she needs to find food immediately. She feeds on nectar and begins to look for a nesting site. She flies just over the ground surface looking for and going into rodent holes to see if they are suitable for nesting. Many queens nest in old rodent holes because they contain straw, fur and hay which can be used as insulation for the nest. Queens cannot bring in their own nesting material so they

Bombus hypnorum—Tree bumblebee guard workers at the entrance to their nest in a tit nest box. © Nick Withers

need to nest where a rodent, previous bumblebee colony or bird (in the case of tit nest boxes) has nested. The British species except carder bumblebees and the Tree bumblebee *Bombus hypnorum,* usually nest underground. Carder bumblebees nest on the ground surface, weaving grass stems together and making their nest inside. They often nest around fence posts and in rough tussock grass. *B. hypnorum* nests in old woodpecker holes, but will also use tit nest boxes. Queens of *B. hypnorum* are quite opportunistic and many nest in loft insulation, old sofas and have even been found in disused tumble driers. Sometimes queens of other species are also to be found in these locations. Many of the early emergers nest in our gardens, such as under paving stones, rockeries and sheds. Less is known about where the late emergers nest. The nest entrance hole tends to be inconspicuous so not easily seen by predators. Some daughter queens may go back to their maternal nest or nest in another empty bumblebee nest but this will depend on nesting availability in the area.

Once the queen has found her nest site she flies slowly in widening circles and arcs near the nest entrance, facing it, orientating to learn the visual cues of the surroundings, so she can find the entrance again. She then begins to collect pollen; some of this she will eat herself to develop her ovaries which have shrunk during hibernation (she had mated before entering hibernation). When her ovaries are ready she starts to secrete wax from her abdomen to make a nectar pot, which she fills with nectar.

Pocket maker colonies mass the pollen together and then the queen lays eggs on top of it so the hatchling larvae can feed themselves. Pollen storer colonies store the pollen in wax pots and feed their larvae directly as they do with nectar.

Colony structure and foraging
The queen incubates the brood to keep its temperature at 30-32°C. This temperature decreases when she goes out to forage. The eggs hatch into larvae, which feed and then pupate, emerging as workers 5-6 weeks after laying. Once her first brood, of 8-16 workers depending on species, has emerged, the queen remains within the nest and no longer forages. She is able to determine the sex of her offspring and at this stage lays only female-determined eggs which develop into workers. The queen is the dominant or alpha female in the nest. This is maintained not only by her superior size and strength, but by a pheromone (external hormone) which

Incipient *Bombus subterraneus*—Short-haired bumblebee colony
© Nikki Gammans

she produces. This queen pheromone suppresses aggression in the workers towards her and also inhibits development of their ovaries. There is a clear link between ovarian development and increased aggression. The queen is tended by half her workers and the other half forage for the nest. The first brood of workers are often quite small, only being fed on small amounts of pollen which the queen had collected. Before emergence of the first brood takes place, the queen lays more eggs. These hatch into larvae at the same time as the previous generation of larvae become adult workers able to forage for them. As the colony size grows, more food is provided to the young larvae and the resultant worker size therefore increases. The largest workers are often the youngest of the colony. Workers tend to be about one third the size of queens but this will increase through the season.

A nest of some of our most common species with early emerging queens such as the Buff-tailed *Bombus terrestris* or Red-tailed bumblebee *B. lapidarius* may reach worker numbers of 300, even to 400. Late emerging species such as the Short-haired bumblebee *B. subterraneus* or the Ruderal bumblebee *B. ruderatus,* tend to have smaller nests of up to 75-100 workers.

As the colony matures, worker production stops and the new generation of sexuals (males and then new queens) is produced. The tipping point for this sudden change may be a drop in the amount of the pheromone produced by the queen as she ages. First the males are produced. These are haploid, having half the number of chromosomes of the females (workers and queens). Once hatched they may help tend the nest but soon leave not to return. Males have no pollen baskets and do not forage for the colony; their only role in life is to mate with the new queens from other nests. For new queen production to take place, the old queen has to completely cease to produce her pheromone. This enables the rearing of queen larvae. But when it happens some of the larger workers gradually become less inhibited and start competing to lay eggs as their ovaries develop, eating the eggs of their rivals. The old queen's powers decline and she may be assassinated by her own workers. By this time however, the new queen brood has pupated, ensuring the next generation. The young queens once emerged may forage for the nest and help with incubation for a few days. They will then leave the nest to find a male to mate with. A queen bumblebee normally mates with only one male. She then feeds for a day or two and either goes into hibernation or starts a new colony if conditions are favourable. The males live for about 7-12 days and their fertility is at its peak between 3-7 days and decreases thereafter. Males have different strategies for trying to mate with queens

♂ *Bombus lapidarius*— Red-tailed bumblebee © Geoff Allen

depending on their species. For example in the Tree bumblebee *Bombus hypnorum,* the males 'nest entrance gather' outside and try to get in to mate with the new queens. The workers which guard the nest entrance against non-nest mates will drive them off, but some may well get through into the nest. When a queen emerges she will be jumped on by a male, fall to the ground and mate. Males of the Short-haired bumblebee *B. subterraneus* and Great yellow bumblebee *B. distinguendus* also 'nest entrance gather' to wait for the females to emerge, or try to get into the nest to mate with a queen before

CHAPTER 1 ABOUT BUMBLEBEES

Pairing in *Bombus terrestris*—Buff-tailed bumblebee © Sarah Seymour

she emerges. Males of the Red-shanked carder bee *B. ruderarius* fly in groups along hedgerows or shrubs patrolling for queens; this can be called 'male group patrolling'. In most bumblebee species the males individually patrol circuits where queens are likely to be, marking prominent objects such as large stones with a scent pheromone. The height at which the males patrol is dependent on the species.

Many of the early emerging species have two colony cycles within a year; the Buff-tailed bumblebee *Bombus terrestris* may even have a third in mild winters. The late emergers have only one colony cycle and new queens go straight into hibernation to emerge the next year.

Apart from dividing bumblebees into early and late emergers, we can also divide them into having short or long tongues. Long-tongued bumblebees need to forage from flowers with long corollas and short-tongued ones, from short corollas. So for example, foxgloves which have a long corolla, are pollinated by long-tongued bumblebees such as the Garden bumblebee *Bombus hortorum*, Ruderal bumblebee *B. ruderatus* and the Short-haired bumblebee *B. subterraneus*. Flowers such as white clover with shorter corollas are pollinated by short-tongued bees such as the Buff-tailed *B. terrestris* and the Early bumblebee *B. pratorum*. For the length of tongue of individual species please refer to Chapter 4 profiles.

THE BUMBLEBEES OF KENT

Colony and queen survival

Many factors affect the survival of a colony and of an individual queen. Of the queens entering hibernation it is estimated that only 50% survive to emerge in the spring. Reasons for death in hibernation include: lack of fat storage (not enough food whilst in the larval stage), fungal infections and flooding of the hibernation site. Once a queen emerges from hibernation she must find food quickly to replace body fat; if this is lacking in the area or she is too weak to fly, she may die immediately. Some queens may also be attacked by great tits or be infected by a parasite or virus—please refer to the section below on Bumblebee associations for more detail. Once a queen has started a colony she needs to incubate her nest and forage for their food; the temperature of her brood drops whilst she is out foraging and if too cold may die. Continuous forage is needed for a colony through the lifecycle of 3-5 months; if this is lacking at any one stage the colony may starve and die. Of course, weather has a large impact on colony and queen survival. Cold temperatures and wet weather may prevent many species from foraging and lack of food storage can cause colony starvation. At the other extreme it may be too hot for bumblebees to fly (normally over 30°C) or drought may reduce the amount of nectar produced by plants, reducing food availability.

Cuckoo bumblebees

♀ *Bombus terrestris* —
Buff-tailed bumblebee © Geoff Allen

♀ *Bombus vestalis* — Vestal cuckoo bee
note the lack of pollen baskets © Geoff Allen

Cuckoo bees are named after the bird. Cuckoo bumblebee species do not form a colony like the other 'true' social species. They have evolved to become parasites of the social species. In these cuckoos there are only males and females, no worker caste. The female enters a host colony and kills, dislodges or dominates the queen, laying her own eggs inside the nest and letting the workers of the parasitised nest look after them. The female cuckoo often waits around the edges of the nest before fully entering, to obtain the colony odour of the nest. She is then less likely to be challenged by the workers because she has the scent 'badge' of the colony. It is important for the cuckoo to time her entrance into the nest. If too early, the queen may not yet have any workers and if she kills the queen, she will not be able to feed her own brood or the host worker brood because she cannot forage for food. The female cuckoo bee does not have pollen baskets but only the remnants, where she was once a social queen. If she leaves the parasitism too late the host colony may become quite large and she is more likely to be spotted by workers and killed. It is thought the optimum time to parasitise the nest is when the first worker brood has just emerged from their pupae. The female cuckoo also lacks the wax producing glands so she must use some of the social queen's cells into which to lay her eggs.

THE BUMBLEBEES OF KENT

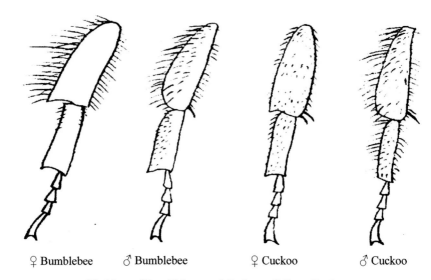

♀ Bumblebee   ♂ Bumblebee   ♀ Cuckoo   ♂ Cuckoo

Hind legs of Bumblebees and Cuckoos © Dave Goulson

Cuckoo bumblebees are also different in their body structure to social bumblebees. As a parasite of a social colony they are adapted for combat with the host queen. They have a thicker layer of chitin on their body which acts like armour, and are less hairy compared to social queens. They also have stronger mandibles (jaws) and a longer sting compared to social queens. The females also have fewer hairs on their legs yet the male cuckoo has more than a social male. They have darker wing membranes which often appear smoky in appearance. All cuckoo bees have short tongues.

Each cuckoo species has a rather narrow range of hosts, usually confining itself to one species or subgenus. For example, *Bombus campestris* parasitises mainly carder bees and usually, the Common carder *B. pascuorum*. *Bombus sylvestris* usually parasitises the subgenus *Pyrobombus* although *B. hypnorum* is so far not a known host. *Bombus vestalis* is mainly a parasite of *B. terrestris* but on occasion has been found in *B. lucorum* nests. The latter is usually a host of *Bombus bohemicus*.

Anatomy

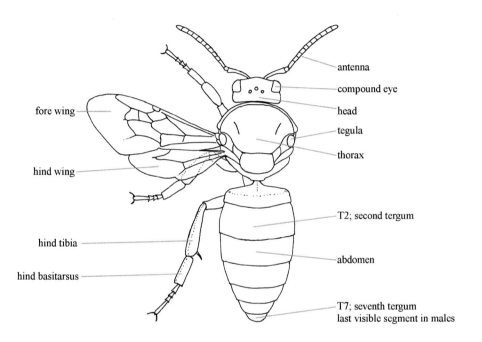

Dorsal view of a ♂ bumblebee with hair removed   © Geoff Allen

A basic anatomy

The above diagram of a male bumblebee shows the location of the basic parts of the bee for field identification. The bee can be seen to be composed of three basic body regions, which can be called, for the sake of simplicity, the head, thorax and abdomen. The thorax has the legs and wings joined to it, whilst the head bears the antennae and eyes. The thorax and abdomen are connected by the wasp waist.

THE BUMBLEBEES OF KENT

For field identification it may be important to find the tegulae on the thorax. These are a pair of small "plates" (sclerites) at the sides of the top of the thorax, each shaped like the upturned saucer of a gravy boat or a segment of a rugby football, which protect the fore wing bases. They are apparent under low magnification, although somewhat hidden by the bee's hair.

The 'collar' of the bee is a hair stripe found at the top front of the thorax just behind the head, often stretching round the thorax in an arc each side to the tegulae. When present the collar is often yellow in colour and can be important in identification. There is sometimes a second stripe at the back of the thorax, of the same colour.

The upper part of the second segment of the abdomen, in this book called T2, often bears a yellow hair band important in identification, as can one on T1. The "tail" of the bumblebee is usually defined as T4-T6 in females and T4-T7 in males (which have an extra segment in the abdomen and indeed 13 antennal segments rather than the 12 in females). The tail often has differently coloured hair to the rest of the abdomen, which can also be important for identification.

The abdomen has the sex organs at the tip; in the male this refers to the genital capsule, sometimes used in advanced identification under the microscope, and the sting in queens and workers. The sting is derived from the egg laying apparatus of the female (the ovipositor) and so only the female castes can sting. Please do not be fooled by myths that bumblebees cannot sting; both co-authors can personally vouch for the fact that they can and do, although only under severe provocation. For this reason, do not handle bumblebees in the field, particularly if you suffer from allergic reactions to other insect stings or bites.

Finally, the tibiae of the female hind legs each have a 'pollen basket' or corbicula. These structures carry the packed pollen back to the nest. The colour of the corbicular hairs is used to separate the females of the Red-tailed bumblebee *Bombus lapidarius* from the Red-shanked carder bee *Bombus ruderarius* in the field. The corbicula is somewhat indicated in the males although not formed for the purpose of pollen carrying.

An intermediate anatomy

Whilst we do not wish to burden the reader with too many details on bumblebee classification, it should be pointed out that anatomical structure and classification go hand in hand. Bumblebees are recognised as such because they have a series of structural features, called characters, in common; other bees will either lack one or more of these characters, or have them expressed in a different form.

Bumblebees are typical insects in as much as their structure conforms to the basic ground plan of insects, i.e. they have three sections (called tagmata) to the body – the head, thorax and abdomen. The head bears a pair of compound eyes, three simple eyes (ocelli) arranged in a triangle at the top of the head between the compound eyes, a pair of antennae and a pair of mandibles which chew from side to side. The bees have another section of the mouthparts formed into a tongue. The first elongate segment of the antenna is called the scape.

The thorax is composed of three segments, the pro-, meso- and metathorax, each with a pair of legs. The second and third segments also each have a pair of wings.

The abdominal segments each have an upper and lower sclerite (cuticular plates); in modern terminology these are called terga and

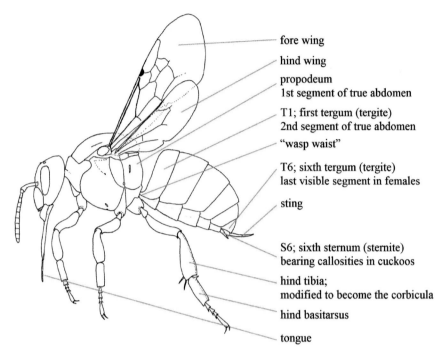

fore wing

hind wing

propodeum
1st segment of true abdomen

T1; first tergum (tergite)
2nd segment of true abdomen

"wasp waist"

T6; sixth tergum (tergite)
last visible segment in females

sting

S6; sixth sternum (sternite)
bearing callosities in cuckoos

hind tibia;
modified to become the corbicula

hind basitarsus

tongue

Side view of a ♀ short-tongued bumblebee with hair removed © Geoff Allen

sterna respectively. In female bumblebees, there are six visible terga (T1-T6) and sterna (S1-S6), and in the males, seven (T1-T7 and S1-S7).

The bees are placed in the insect order Hymenoptera. The prerequisite characters needed by an insect to be placed in this order are in the wings, as described at the start of this chapter, on the Evolution of the bees.

In the suborder Apocrita, the wasp-waisted Hymenoptera, there is a constriction between the first and second segments of the abdomen, forming a waist. The hind segment of the thorax, the metathorax, is broadly fused to the first segment of the abdomen, called the propodeum. The three thoracic segments plus the propodeum together form a composite unit sometimes called the "mesosoma" or "alitrunk". The remainder of the abdomen, also looking like an integral unit, can be called the "metasoma" or "gaster". In the second, more primitive, suborder of Hymenoptera, the Symphyta, the wasp waist is lacking.

In most Apocrita, the ovipositor is used to lay eggs, either into plant tissue (gall wasps) or more often into another insect as in the case of the ichneumons, braconids and chalcids. However, in one group of Apocrita, the ovipositor is no longer used for egg-laying but is formed into the sting, used for hunting and/or defence. These are the stinging insects or aculeates. The hunting wasps use their sting to paralyse the prey, to provision their nest cells for feeding the young, their larvae. In bees, which do not feed their larvae on insects, the sting is solely for defence.

The bumblebee genus *Bombus* is a constituent part of the corbiculate bee subfamily, Apinae. The corbiculate bees have the female hind tibia modified into the corbicula or pollen basket: it is flat and broad, the outer side being shiny and very hairless, and lined top and bottom with a row of stiff curved hairs which hold the collected pollen in place while it is transported to the nest. The exceptions to the possession of a corbicula in the Apinae, are in those females which do not forage for pollen; the cuckoos and the queens of the perennial, eusocial bees, i.e. the stingless bees and honeybees. The males always lack the corbicula, never foraging for their colony.

Advanced anatomy
An advanced anatomy is beyond the scope of this book and so the reader is referred to works such as Gauld and Bolton (1996) and the big generic revisions of various families of aculeate Hymenoptera. Gauld and Bolton defines an enormous number of technical terms used in anatomy and classification (the science of taxonomy) and in behaviour. It would be daunting to the beginner but nevertheless is a milestone in the taxonomy

of the Hymenoptera.

However, it can be said that classification is closely correlated with and dependent on anatomical structure, and that the correlation, using cladistics, seeks to tie in, usually successfully, with ideas on evolution.

Bumblebee associations

Predators of adult bumblebees and their nests

Although conveniently dealt with here, predation is not strictly an association unless the predator is specialist on one sort of prey.

In the last decade, dead queen bumblebees have been observed with their abdomen cut at the tail. This strange phenomenon has now been attributed to great tits. It appears the tits have learnt to cut the tail of emerging queens and remove the organs leaving just the shell of the abdomen. Why have great tits started this behaviour? Perhaps it is due to insect food shortage and having to forage on more marginal species. In the UK no other bird species are known to do this; it is possible that vagrant species such as bee-eaters and shrikes may take adult bumblebees but most of these prefer honeybees. In fact not many species use adult bumblebees as food, preferring to attack the nest where the brood and honey are stored. The larvae and pupae of the bees are soft and full of protein as opposed to the adult which has a shell made of chitin, indigestible to many species. The main species which attack bumblebee nests are mammals, such as mice, foxes and badgers. When nests are destroyed by badgers, a huge hole is found where the nest was and a few very confused bumblebees are left behind. Small rodents such as field mice are the most frequent of attackers but would not be so obvious to an observer.

CHAPTER 1 ABOUT BUMBLEBEES

A few generalist predatory insects are large and powerful enough to tackle individual social bees and wasps. The predator generally takes its prey in flight. One or two of the larger robber flies (Diptera: Asilidae), but particularly *Asilus crabroniformis*, have been recorded taking *Bombus* workers, as well as those of *Apis mellifera* and a queen of *Vespula germanica*. Some of the larger dragonflies (Odonata: Anisoptera) fall in the same category. However, a remarkable observation was of a worker social wasp stinging a dragonfly which had attempted to predate it, killing and then butchering it. It is doubtful, though, if a bumblebee could deploy its sting to strike like this.

Brood predators

The Wax moth *Aphomia sociella* (Lepidoptera: Pyralidae, Galleriinae) is a serious pest of bumblebees and also attacks social wasps (Hymenoptera: Vespidae). The female moth is said to invade the nest of the host and lay its eggs in masses on the wax cells. The hatching moth larvae first feed gregariously on old cells and detritus but when larger, turn their attention to the brood cells, burrowing in silk-lined tunnels to eat the bee larvae and pupae. When fully fed they leave the nest and spin cocoons in a group under cover. They do not pupate in their cocoon until the following year, when they emerge to carry out the next cycle. It is unclear why the guard workers do not manage to kill the adult female moth as she invades.

The "velvet ant" *Mutilla europaea* (Hymenoptera: Mutillidae) (actually a wasp) with its armoured exoskeleton and powerful sting, invades the nests of bumblebees and lays its eggs in the cell clusters of the bee nest. Each larva of the velvet ant feeds on a pupa of the bee, causing its death. The female *Mutilla* is wingless, whilst the male is fully winged. *Mutilla* is scarce in Kent and its distribution mirrors that of the carder bee *Bombus humilis*.

THE BUMBLEBEES OF KENT

♂ Velvet ant *Mutilla europaea* © Peter Maton

Endoparasites and endoparasitoids

Nematode worms have long been known as internal parasites (endoparasites) of a variety of insects and *Sphaerularia bombi* is to be found in *Bombus* queens. One to several female nematodes enter a queen's body as she hibernates and develop. When this queen emerges in the spring she feeds and the nematodes, situated in her gaster, lay eggs. As the season progresses, the eggs hatch and the juvenile nematodes develop. The nematode alters the behaviour of the bee and instead of founding a nest she digs into a site used by hibernating queens and dies. The nematodes leave her body, moulting twice and mating. The fertilised female nematodes then wait for new queens to come to hibernate in the autumn.

The thick-headed or big-headed flies (Diptera: Conopidae) are a family with some 25 British species. The habits of several species are known and most are internal parasitoids (endoparasitoids) of aculeates. At least four genera, *Conops, Myopa, Physocephala* and *Sicus* have species which attack bumblebee workers during the summer months, although other species in some of these genera will use worker social wasps. The female fly has a dagger-like ovipositor and attacks the aculeate from above and behind, often in flight, seizing it and laying an egg through an intersegmental membrane (i.e. between two of the abdominal terga). The hatching fly larva feeds at first in the haemocoel of the host but then on the internal organs of the abdomen. The fly larva alters the behaviour of the parasitised bee, so that it seeks out a safe place for the parasite to complete its development, before itself dying (Benton, 2006).

The parasitoid wasp *Syntretus splendidus* (Hymenoptera: Braconidae, Euphorinae) is believed to attack bumblebees in the same way as Conopidae, but it is the rather later emerging spring queens, such as *Bombus pascuorum,* which are often attacked. In the very early emerging *B. terrestris* and *B. lucorum,* foraging workers are the main victims. Faster foraging species, such as *B. hortorum*, may be less likely to be attacked The egg laying has not been observed but it is likely the female *Syntretus* seizes the foraging host bee to lay. The eggs are often found in the thoracic cavity and may be introduced through the membranous tissue of the neck. In a queen there may be more than 70 eggs whilst in the smaller workers there are usually less than 20. The eggs increase in size by absorbing nutrients from the host haemolymph. The hatched larvae are generally found in the bee's abdomen. They do not feed on the host's viscera but are still surrounded by the embryonic membrane from the egg, the cells of which absorb fat from the host's body fluid. The larvae feed on these hypertrophied cells and when mature, break out of the dying bee's abdomen via the intersegmental membrane between the first and second terga, to pupate. From the egg-laying to emergence takes 10 days (Alford, 1975). There are about 20 European species of *Syntretus* but there is only biological information for two. The other known species, *S. xanthocephalus* (= *lyctaea*), has been reared from an adult ichneumonid (van Achterberg and Haeselbarth, 2003). There is active research into *Syntretus* at present, because of its economic implications.

Commensals

These are organisms which live for all or part of their life cycle in association with another species, the commensal benefiting from the association

♀ *Bombus terrestris*—Buff-tailed bumblebee carrying *Parasitellus* mites
© Siew Lee Vorley

tion but importantly, the host not being harmed or losing fitness. This is not parasitism, where the host is harmed. *Parasitellus* species (Acarina: Parasitidae) are common but harmless mites found in the deutonymph (second larval) stage on queen bumblebees in the spring; this deutonymph stage is non-feeding. When the queen begins nest foundation the mites crawl off her body and to the bottom of the new nest, where they act as detritus feeders. Several generations of mites are produced over the period of nesting. When the nest cycle ends mites climb onto the newly reared queens to over winter, completing the life cycle. There are a number of other mite genera associated with bumblebees. We are often asked if the parasitic honeybee mite *Varroa destructor* is also a pest of bumblebees. *Bombus* queens sometimes carry this mite: it is thought that the bumblebee could pick up the mite when raiding weak honeybee colonies for nectar in the spring. Also, a bumblebee could pick up the mite whilst visiting a flower just after an infested honeybee. The mite does not affect bumblebees because the nests do not overwinter unlike those of honeybees: the *Varroa* need to be on warm bees during the winter. Also *Varroa* does not multiply in bumblebee brood.

The larvae of several species of fly inhabit bumblebee nests, where they are detritus feeders. Examples include *Volucella bombylans* (Diptera: Syrphidae) and the Lesser house flies *Fannia* spp (Diptera: Fanniidae). The adult female *Volucella* enters the nest tunnel, running the gauntlet of

♀ *Volucella bombylans "plumata"* — a hoverfly © Jeremy Early

the guard bees and flips her eggs into the nest. The eggs have a sticky coating which quickly dries, gluing them to the nest material. If the *Volucella* is killed by the guard workers, she continues to lay eggs by a reflex action. The hatching larvae live at the bottom of the comb, where they are apparently undetected. They will occasionally feed on cell clusters containing the bee brood. They pupate after finishing feeding and emerge the following year. The fact that they will sometimes feed on brood means that they can act as both commensals and brood predators, and this could explain why the bees are so vindictive towards the adult fly.

Social parasites or inquilines (cuckoos)

The cuckoo bumblebees are important parasites. The female cuckoo usurps the role of the host queen, often killing her in the process. The cuckoo does not have a worker caste of her own; the host workers rear her brood, and only males and females are produced. Although cuckoo bumblebees have comparatively short tongues, they are thought to have been evolutionarily derived from among the long-tongued species.

THE BUMBLEBEES OF KENT

Disease transfer from honeybees to bumblebees
New research has suggested that diseases can cross from honeybees to bumblebees; in particular deformed wing virus (DWV) and a fungal parasite called *Nosema ceranae*. Researchers at Royal Holloway University of London have found that these pathogens affect adult bumblebees as well as honeybees (M.J.F. Brown, *pers. comm.*). In honeybees the presence of DWV along with the parasitic mite *Varroa* can cause entire colonies to collapse. Although as stated above, *Varroa* does not affect bumblebee colonies (as it needs to overwinter on the warm adult honeybees), DWV can affect the colony by reducing the lifespan of individual workers. As many bumblebee species have small numbers of workers this could have a significant effect on foraging efficiency of the colony and long term colony survival. More research is needed on the impacts of pathogens on bumblebees.

Batesian mimicry
A number of harmless insects mimic bumblebees to gain protection from predation by vertebrates. These are examples of Batesian mimicry. Many are syrphid flies, a family in which many of the species mimic one aculeate or another. The best known case is in *Volucella*, where two species resemble the hornet *Vespa crabro*, whilst *Volucella bombylans* is very bumblebee-like. The commensalism of the larvae of *V. bombylans* has been dealt with earlier. The adult is found in several colour forms, each of which resembles a different species of bumblebee. This is a common theme in *Bombus*-mimicking Syrphidae, where a number of species each have several colour forms, sometimes strikingly different from each other.

Some Syrphidae have no connection with bumblebees other than to resemble one species or another. A common example is *Merodon equestris*, the Greater bulb fly. The mimicry can be striking, the resting fly when disturbed behaving like a bumble, to the extent of raising a middle

CHAPTER 1 ABOUT BUMBLEBEES

Females of two colour forms of *Merodon equestris*, the Greater bulb fly © Jeremy Early

leg as in the threat posture of a resting bee.

The rare staphylinid beetle, *Emus hirtus*, generally resembles a bumble-bee but its behaviour is not similar in any way, laying its eggs in cow pats.

Mullerian mimicry

A few solitary bees are very similar in general appearance to bumble-bees; these are cases of Mullerian mimicry, i.e. both are stinging insects. The resemblance probably means that vertebrate predators have fewer aposematic (warning) colour patterns to learn. A good example is the

♀ *Anthophora plumipes*—Hairy-footed flower bee © Nick Withers

Hairy-footed flower bee *Anthophora plumipes*, where the female is all black haired with reddish scopal hairs, perhaps resembling *Bombus ruderatus*, whilst the male is brown haired like a carder bee. Another species of *Anthophora*, namely A. *furcata*, somewhat resembles the Shrill carder bee *Bombus sylvarum*.

THE BUMBLEBEES OF KENT

A resemblance of a similar kind is often found within the bumblebees themselves. It is mentioned that the females of the Red-tailed bumblebee *Bombus lapidarius* look very similar to those of Red-shanked carder bee *B. ruderarius* but these are not closely related bees within the genus. The extinct *B. cullumanus* and *B. pomorum* also bore a resemblance to these as does the cuckoo *B. rupestris.* Most of these bumblebees are only distantly related to each other within *Bombus* and hence are examples of Mullerian mimicry. Closely related species do not necessarily resemble one another. For example, in the subgenus *Bombus (Pyrobombus)*, *Bombus hypnorum* could easily be mistaken for a carder bumblebee, whilst *B. pratorum* and *B. monticola* do resemble each other, with yellow bands and a red tail. The fourth British species in this group, *B. jonellus,* has yellow bands but a white tail, and the male could pass for a small *B. lucorum* or *B. hortorum.* In some of the Northern and Western Isles, however, *B. jonellus* males can have a red tail, strongly resembling those of *B. pratorum*, and both red and white tailed forms may be reared from the same nest.

CHAPTER 2
PEOPLE AND BUMBLEBEES

Importance of bumblebees

Animal pollination contributes to an estimated 35% of global crop production. Bees are thought to be the most important of the animal pollinators but flies, moths, butterflies, beetles and bats are also pollinators. Bees are important pollinators of many of our wildflowers (80%) and high value agricultural crops (84%). This free service the bees (and other insects) provide is currently estimated to be worth £560 million per year to the UK economy and €14.2 billion to the European economy per year. It is important to conserve all bee species, solitary, honeybee and bumblebee because of their differing tongue lengths. This allows pollination of different crops and wildflowers with their different corolla lengths.

It is known that pollination increases most crop yields. Research on strawberries demonstrated that plants pollinated by bees resulted in heavier, higher commercial grade fruit, with fewer malformations. They also had increased redness, reduced sugar-acid ratio and were firmer which increased the shelf life, reducing waste.

Bumblebees in particular are important pollinators due to buzz pollination or sonication. Crops such as tomatoes, blueberries, cranberries and strawberries hold the pollen very tightly onto their anthers. When a bumblebee lands on the flower it dislocates its wing muscles and vibrates its body causing the anther to vibrate releasing its pollen. About 8% of the world's flowers are primarily pollinated by sonication. In the UK, only bumblebees can perform this action.

Bumblebees due to their ability to raise their body temperature, by buzzing their wing muscles with the insulation of their fur, can also forage at much lower temperatures than honeybees and solitary bees, increasing their pollination services. Some bumblebee species, such as the Buff-tailed bumblebee *B. terrestris,* can forage during the winter months in snow.

Their decline and reasons why

Since the 1930s, with agricultural intensification and increasing urbanisation, the UK has lost over 97% of its ancient wild flower meadows. This has greatly reduced the foraging and nesting habitats for many of our bumblebee species. In particular, the bumblebee species which require open meadow habitat have been those which have declined the most. The rapid loss of this habitat is thought to have resulted in a decline in approximately 32% of our UK bee species.

Other impacts on bumblebee populations are parasites and predators which have been discussed in Chapter 1. Other potential harmful impacts on bumblebees are pesticides.

How we can help reverse the declines

Gardening for bumblebees

With the loss of over 97% of the UK's wild flower meadows, gardens are playing an increasingly important role. They are a natural mosaic and corridor across the country and cover more hectares than all of our nature reserves put together. They are an important resource for many of our bumblebee species. Many of our most common bumblebees rely on gardens for their food and nesting sites and often these species are now doing better in gardens than in the open countryside. With the right mix of flowers it is possible to have up to 9 species of bumblebees in your garden.

Bumblebees are generalist species meaning they will forage on a variety of flowers but their tongue length will dictate which flowers they can visit. Bees with a long tongue will visit long corolla flowers and those

CHAPTER 2   PEOPLE AND BUMBLEBEES

Worker *Bombus hortorum*—Garden
bumblebee © Sarah Seymour

♂ *Bombus terrestris* — Buff-tailed bumblebee © Sarah Seymour

with short tongues, short corollas. To finish their colonies and produce
the next generation of sexuals (new queens and males) bumblebees need
continuous forage through their flight periods of March-September,
which gardens can provide.

In March-April good sources for bumblebees are heathers, pussy willow
and cherry. In May-June leguminous plants such as the clovers, tomatoes, thyme and foxgloves are ideal sources. From July through to September lavender, teasel and borage are good. Examples of suitable forage
are given in the table below.

THE BUMBLEBEES OF KENT

March-April

Apple
Bluebell
Broom
Bugle
Cherry

Heather
Flowering currant
Lungwort
Pear
White dead-nettle

Pussy willow
Red dead-nettle
Rosemary
Plum

May- June

Alliums
Aquilegia
Birds-foot trefoil
Bush vetch
Ceanothus
Campanula
Chives
Comfrey
Meadow cranesbill
Cotoneaster
Red clover
Meadow vetchling
Tomatoes

Everlasting pea
Everlasting wallflower
Foxglove
Geranium
Honeysuckle
Kidney vetch
Lupin
Ground ivy
Poppies
Dog rose
Raspberries
Yellow flag iris
Field bean

Red campion
Roses
Sage
Salvia
Thyme
Tufted vetch
White clover
Monkshood
Wisteria
Woundwort
Escallonia
Courgette
Stachys

July-September

Black horehound
Borage
Bramble
Buddleia
Cardoon
Catmint
Mint
Sunflower
Teasel
Thistles
Vipers bugloss
Red bartsia

Knapweed
Lambs ear
Lavender
Lesser Burdock
Marjoram
Mellilot
St. Johns wort
Heathers
Hebe
Hollyhock
Hyssop

Rock rose
Sainfoin
Scabious
Sea holly
Snapdragons
Cornflower
Delphinium
Penstemon
Polemonium
Purple loosestrife
Privet

CHAPTER 2   PEOPLE AND BUMBLEBEES

What to do if you find a bumblebee nest in your garden

Most colonies of bumblebees will only live for 3-4 months. Often when a nest is noticed it is already at the peak of its worker production and may only have between 2-3 weeks left to live. Bumblebees are not aggressive and a nest can be observed from a distance of 1-2 metres by children and adults. However, caution is advised for the Tree bumblebee *Bombus hypnorum* as the colonies can be more defensive. It is recommended that a bumblebee colony is left to finish its cycle and it should be regarded as a positive thing to have in a garden. Occasionally new queen bumblebees will return to their maternal nest; if a further nest is not wanted in that place it can be sealed up once all activity has ceased.

Nesting places for bumblebees and solitary bees

Bumblebees normally nest where something else has nested before, such as rodents. As bumblebees cannot bring in their own nesting material they need fur, hay or straw as nest insulation. They will normally nest under paving stones, rockeries, sheds or even in blue tit boxes. There are bumblebee boxes available to buy in gardening centres; however many of these are unsuitable for bumblebees because the nest entrance is too obvious to nest predators such as the wax moth. An alternative option is to try a blue tit nest box and place it south to south-east facing. If you would like a bumblebee nest, leave the nesting material from a blue tit, otherwise clean it out (this is a general rule). Another option which may work is using an upturned plant pot and placing rodent nesting material inside (as from a pet shop) and dig a hose to come out of the plant pot as the entrance hole. For more information refer to the website of the Bumblebee Conservation Trust: http://bumblebeeconservation.org/

THE BUMBLEBEES OF KENT

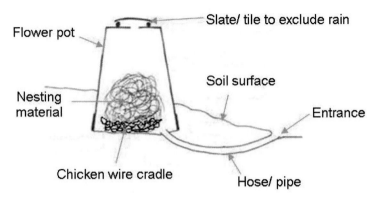

Flower pot

Slate/ tile to exclude rain

Nesting material

Soil surface

Entrance

Chicken wire cradle

Hose/ pipe

Flower pot nest © Bumblebee Conservation Trust

Solitary bee hotels work very well as nesting habitat for leafcutter bees and mason bees. Place 6ft high in a south to south-east direction to catch the morning sun. Many of the holes will fill up after a short time. These hotels can be brought from most garden centres or alternatively you can make your own by drilling holes of a diameter of 3-4mm to 12.5mm into old logs or timber and placed in the above position.

Solitary bee hotel and a leafcutter bee using a bamboo cane © Nikki Gammans

CHAPTER 2   PEOPLE AND BUMBLEBEES

Creating a wild flower area in your garden

To create a wild flower area within your garden you will need to choose an area in full sunlight. The best times to sow seeds are either in April or preferably from Mid-July to Mid-August/beginning September (so they will have enough leaflets before the first frost, e.g. red clover and for the frost to break their dormancy e.g. yellow rattle). To prepare the area mow the lawn very short, remove all cuttings and rake the soil to agitate the surface creating bare ground. Broadcast the seeds on the soil surface, gently tread the seeds in and then water.

Alternatively sow the wild flower seeds in a seed tray and plant out as plug plants. Seeds can be sown from April onwards and planted out when growth is suitable. Prepare the planting area as above.

Once established, the area should be cut at the end of June/July and all cuttings removed, allowed to re-flower and then cut again when the flowers have set seed. Always remove cuttings. An April cut may also be needed if the grass sward begins to dominate.

Farming for bumblebees

Many of our rare bumblebee species are open landscape nesters and foragers that need flower-rich habitats to survive. Farm land can be an important food source and nesting site for many species. Recreating flower-rich habitat across a farming landscape has proven to be successful in increasing populations of many rare bumblebees such as *Bombus ruderatus*, the Ruderal bumblebee. Grants are available through agri-environment schemes to create pollen and nectar strips around arable fields and flower rich hay meadows in pastoral lands. More information about agri-environment schemes can be found on the Natural England and the Short-haired bumblebee project websites.

THE BUMBLEBEES OF KENT

Pollen and nectar strip at an arable field margin, Brissenden Farm © Nikki Gammans

The Short-haired bumblebee project

The Short-haired bumblebee project was formed in 2009 by Natural England, RSPB, Bumblebee Conservation Trust and Hymettus to reintroduce an extinct UK bumblebee species, the Short-haired bumblebee *Bombus subterraneus*. This bee was last recorded in Dungeness, Kent in 1988 and was officially declared extinct in 2000 by the IUCN (International Union for the Conservation of Nature). The bee is also declining across its native European range except for some Baltic countries. It is thought that agricultural intensification and increasing urbanisation has removed large extents of habitat required by this bee.

The project's primary aim is to successfully reintroduce *Bombus subter-*

raneus back to the UK to form a self-sufficient, self-sustainable population. In order for the population to survive, the project works with farmers, land owners and conservation groups to recreate, and to give advice on seed sowing and management of flower rich habitat. With a large group of volunteers, the project also completes bumblebee surveys across the release zone of Dungeness and Romney Marsh to establish the response of bumblebees to the increasing flower rich habitat.

The queens are reintroduced to the UK from populations in Skåne, Sweden. In Sweden, the *B. subterraneus* population is expanding and has recolonized Norway since going extinct there in the 1950s. Permission was given to the project to collect 100 queens a year, 0.1% of the population in the Skåne province of Sweden for reintroduction.

The queens are collected emerging from hibernation in April/May, depending on Spring temperatures (queens begin to emerge over 18°C). Areas are walked looking for queens where there are white dead nettle *Lamium album* and comfrey *Symphytum* sp flowering (the favourite early flowering forage plants of emerging *B. subterraneus* queens). Queens are collected using a butterfly net and each stored in a honeybee queen rearing vial. They are checked to see if they have collected any pollen. If they are carrying pollen they are not collected as they have already started a nest and will not nest again. The queens are stored in a fridge at 4-5°C which induces torpor, and are individually fed nightly. After five days of collecting, they are brought back to the UK to begin two weeks of quarantine.

The quarantine is needed to detect any diseases or parasites the queens may have. If affected, they will not be released. It is expected that approximately 50% of emerging queens will have diseases and parasites. The healthy queens are then released at the RSPB Dungeness Nature Reserve where there is ample forage. Plants they will first feed on are red clover *Trifolium pratense*, ground ivy *Glechoma hederacea*, yellow

THE BUMBLEBEES OF KENT

flag iris *Iris pseudacorus*, and foxgloves *Digitalis* sp.

Bumblebee surveys are then walked by the project officer with the project's 24 volunteers across the release zone of Dungeness and Romney Marsh. Areas are surveyed which have been newly created or are under improved management.

A fixed route is walked either fortnightly or monthly and all bumblebee species seen are recorded. Kent and East Sussex were chosen as the release zone as the counties have the highest diversity of rare bumblebees and improving flower rich habitat for the reintroduction would also help these species.

The improvement in flower rich areas managed by farmers, land owners and conservation groups has greatly helped the five rarest species found in Kent, the Shrill carder bee *B. sylvarum*, Brown-banded carder bee *B.*

Wild flower meadow at RSPB Dungeness © Nikki Gammans

humilis, Moss carder bee *B. muscorum*, Ruderal bumblebee *B. ruderatus* and the Red-shanked carder bee *B. ruderarius*. For example, *B. sylvarum* has been recorded in the Dungeness area where it had not been found for over 20 years and another, *B. ruderatus* has been recorded in areas of Dungeness and Romney Marsh where it had not been found for between 10-25 years. It is possible small remnant populations existed, which were so small they were undetected and have now expanded into new areas. Alternatively, the queens could be dispersing into new areas from a greater distance than we have previously expected. Resident populations of *B. humilis* and *B. muscorum*, which were more restricted to coastal communities, have also been found to disperse inland. Populations of *B. ruderarius* have been slower to disperse but populations from the Weald in East Sussex appear to be slowly moving eastwards into Kent.

Habitat improvement has been a key objective of the project and has been achieved through working in partnership with many farmers, conservation groups and local government groups. Advice has been given on seed mixes, sowing times and management to improve areas of flower rich habitat. When the project began in 2009, the aim was to improve and recreate between 20-30 hectares, currently the project has over 850 hectares managed for flowers.

The Project's first worker *Bombus subterraneus*—Short-haired bumblebee, on red clover at RSPB Dungeness © Nick Withers

Since beginning the reintroductions in 2012, seven workers of *B. subterraneus* have been seen. These are the first workers to be recorded in the UK for over 25 years, marking the first significant milestone of the reintroduction project. It is hoped a minimum of five reintroductions at Dungeness and Romney Marsh will achieve a self-sustainable population; however more reintroductions to this site may be necessary to achieve this. The project will then look towards establishing another population within the UK.

The project also organises outreach activities such as working with primary schools through to university level students, giving talks to interested groups, leading bumblebee identification walks, and provides bumblebee identification days.

For current information on the project please visit
www.bumblebeereintroduction.org

Capture and field identification techniques for bumblebees
Trying to photograph bumblebees and insects in general is difficult due to their fast flight with the bumblebees appearing as a fuzzy blob. The best way to get a positive identification is to first net the bee. It should then be placed in a sample tube and identified with a hand lens. Basic nets can be brought with a wooden handle from Watkins and Doncaster. Nets vary in diameter and a size should be chosen which you are most comfortable with. The easiest way to collect a bee from the net is to hold

CHAPTER 2   PEOPLE AND BUMBLEBEES

Holding up the net bag   Bumblebee in queen plunger

Both © Nikki Gammans

the net bag up (while the frame of the net is on the ground) and the bee will fly upwards and towards the sun. The bee can then be caught in the corner of the net with the tube. Place the tube over the bee, with the net covering the top and then put on the tube top. This is quite simple to do but might take some practice.

Any sized sample tube can be used but there must always be air holes drilled into the top. A tissue can also be placed into the tube to stop the bee from flying which makes identification and photography easier. A bee should only be kept within a tube for a minimal amount of time to avoid stressing it. In some circumstances it may be necessary to use a hand lens; a x10 or x20 will suffice. Queen plungers can also be used; this is a plastic tube with fine netting at one end and a plunger with a sponge at one end to immobilise the bee for examination with a hand lens. Using the identification guide in Chapter 4 you should then be able to identify a bumblebee to species.

THE BUMBLEBEES OF KENT

Dispelling myths

This section dispels some of the myths around bumblebees which are thought of as fact.

Bees die when they sting you. This is true for worker honeybees because they have a barbed sting. The honeybee therefore cannot extract its sting and when it is brushed off, the sting, venom sac and some of the viscera are left behind in the wound, pumping in more venom by a reflex action. The injured bee does not die instantaneously. Solitary bees and bumblebees do not have a barbed sting and so it can be extracted after they have stung. This means they can repeatedly sting but this would normally only occur if they felt threatened.

A bumblebee only buzzes when it flies. Bumblebees can buzz when they are not flying because the sound comes from the wing muscles in the thorax, which when vibrating cause air to resonate through the spiracles. Hence their just vibrating the muscles causes this buzzing sound. The bumblebees' buzz is often used in the nest as a defence mechanism. When the colony feels a vibration or believes it may be under attack they will collectively buzz, sounding aggressive and perhaps larger than their actual size. This noise is used to drive away any potential predators.

Bumblebees should not be able to fly according to the laws of physics. It is quite bizarre how this myth has become common belief. Bumblebees can fly according to the law of physics because their wing muscles vibrate not contract and expand like mammals. This vibration, like a rubber band, can increase the number of wing beats per second to 200. The wings are also not in a fixed position; the angle of the wings changes between the up and down strokes of each wing beat. During the down stroke the wings are angled almost horizontally, thus giving the maximum surface area and air resistance for achieving lift. In the up stroke the wings are angled downwards to the rear, to reduce the effective wing area and so minimising drag, and hence there is a net overall

♀ *Bombus subterraneus*—Short-haired bumblebee © Andy Tebbs

lifting effect. (This is somewhat analogous to the oar strokes of a rower, there is maximum drag giving propulsion one way and minimum on the return). Sometimes a queen bumblebee, if having fed heavily, may slightly struggle with her take off. She may veer from side to side but flies straight once she has the right trajectory.

♂ *Bombus terrestris*—Buff-tailed bumblebee © Sarah Seymour

CHAPTER 3
BIOGEOGRAPHY OF THE KENT BUMBLEBEES

Kent in relation to Britain

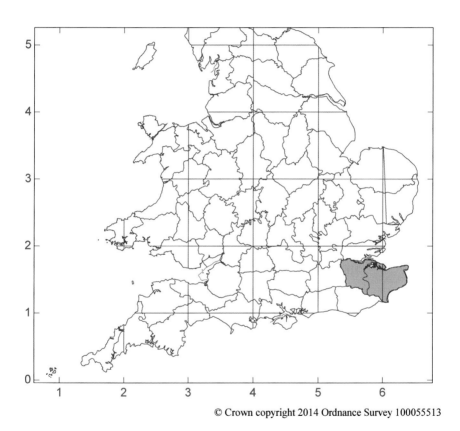

© Crown copyright 2014 Ordnance Survey 100055513

The position of Kent (in grey) in the south-eastern corner of southern Britain is shown on the above map.

The county boundary used in this survey, as those in the Bees, wasps and ants of Kent (Allen, 2009) and the Dragonflies of Kent (Brook and

THE BUMBLEBEES OF KENT

Brook, 2009), is defined by the two Watsonian vice counties: West Kent (vc16) and East Kent (vc15). It includes much of what are now the south -east London boroughs, here called the metropolitan area of West Kent, vc16. The boundary between the two vice counties is defined on the map by the sinuous line going north to south, making East Kent roughly twice the area of West Kent. The area of Kent is superimposed on a vice county map of England and Wales.

The climate of Kent, as that of the adjacent county Surrey (Baldock, 2008), is milder than that of most of Britain due to its southerly position. Indeed Brogdale Farm near Faversham holds the highest temperature record ever found in the UK at 38.5°C (101.3°F) on 10 August 2003, whilst Gravesend had a high of 38.1°C (100.6°F) on the same day.

Unlike Surrey, Kent has an extensive coastline which may further contribute to its mild climate, the seas in winter having a warming effect. Even so, it is not climate which enables Kent to have more bumblebees than Surrey but its extensive coastal grazing marshes and brown field sites. The close proximity of Kent to France means that our county often receives the first wave of colonising species, although this was not true for the Tree bumblebee *Bombus hypnorum* or the Ivy bee *Colletes hederae*.

Principal towns and key bumblebee sites

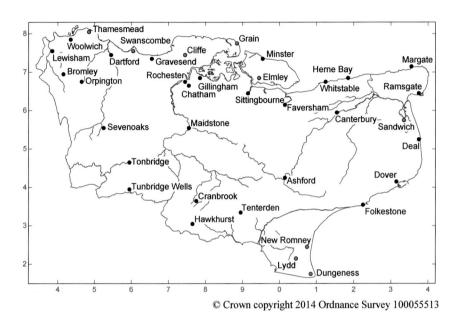

© Crown copyright 2014 Ordnance Survey 100055513

The above map shows the principal towns and villages of Kent located with black dots and some key bumblebee sites given as red dots. Some of the "towns" in the metropolitan area of Watsonian West Kent were visited by Victorian entomologists and produced interesting records. Increasing urbanisation since has meant that much of this interest has been lost, although a number of the early Kent records of *Bombus hypnorum* were from this area (e.g. Lewisham, Upper Sydenham and Crystal Palace Park). Orpington and Dartford are on the outskirts of the metropolitan area.

Rochester, Chatham and Gillingham form another conurbation, now known as the Medway Unitary Authority. The important bumblebee sites on the Hoo peninsula, including Cliffe and Grain marshes, fall in this administrative area.

The other principal human settlements are the city of Canterbury and the towns of Maidstone, Ashford, Sevenoaks, Tonbridge and Tunbridge Wells.

Many of the coastal towns of Kent are popular tourist destinations. Folkestone and Ramsgate were once ports for ferries to the continent and of course, Dover still is, being the main one in the south-east of England. Ramsgate was the port for hovercraft services and the derelict hover-port site is adjacent to an important aculeate site.

It can be seen from the map that most of the key bumblebee sites are coastal and also mainly grazing marshes. The RSPB reserve at Dungeness has been intensively managed for the reintroduction of the Short-haired bumblebee *Bombus subterraneus*, with several fields having excellent expanses of red clover, tufted vetch and other bumblebee plants in readiness. Dungeness has been said to be "the Bumblebee Capital of Britain". The MoD ranges at nearby Lydd have changed but little ecologically for several human generations and augment the RSPB site.

There are also several RSPB reserves on the north Kent marshes and many of these are important for bumblebees, particularly the UK BAP schedule 41 species of carder bee: *Bombus sylvarum*, *B. ruderarius*, *B. humilis* and *B. muscorum*. The first two of these species are threatened almost everywhere in their now limited range in the UK.

The Deal to Sandwich dunes are important sites for aculeates in general as well as for bumblebees.

The authors are of the opinion that there is little correlation between bumblebee distribution and either the underlying geology, Natural England natural areas or Rose's botanical areas, except where these define coastal areas, such as the north Kent marshes and Romney/Walland Marshes. Bumblebees tend to be found by general aculeate recorders who have concentrated their efforts in the more favourable locations, particularly areas receiving good warming from sun light (i.e. high insolation) such as sandy heaths and quarries, possibly skewing the distribution data.

Recording for this book

To prepare the maps in this book, field work and desktop studies were conducted to establish the presence of species in the grid squares. A blank square on a distribution map does not necessarily mean the species does not occur there; merely that it was not spotted during any recording there, if done. Absence can be hard to ascertain in biological recording of insects.

For the monitoring on Romney/Walland Marshes, it was considered desirable to record numbers of each caste of a bumblebee species spotted at a location on a day, this requiring methodical field work and a good means of data storage.

The resolution of the scale used for recording purposes has increased immensely with the advent of hand held GPS devices. A tetrad dot (2km square, e.g. TQ75T) pencilled in on a map card of yesteryear often meant that the recording was done to the same coarse scale. Each dot may have been supported by only one record. Our recording has been done to a minimum of 4 figures e.g. TQ7656 (1km resolution), and usually to 6 figures, such as TQ767564 (100m). This latter is usually sufficient to record strong flying insects like social bees because they sometimes forage some distance from their nest. Greater resolution would be required to pin point a nest site and although GPS devices can locate to 10 figures, there is always a small margin of error in such fine readings.

Problems with recording social insects

Social insects pose problems for recording. It is hard to ascertain true abundance for them as workers are non-reproductive and represent colonies which have only one reproductive female each, the queen. Thus, counting workers does not give a true representation of the species' abundance. It is also very difficult to locate and therefore count bumblebee nests.

Data storage and retrieval

Modern biological recording packages can easily accommodate more than 1 million records; two frequently used ones are MapMate and Recorder 6. One of the co-authors (GWA) tried several options and eventually settled on a FileMaker Pro database dedicated to the British aculeates, devised by Mike and Rowan Edwards. It is generally easy to import records to this cross platform application but configuring the data can be a little time consuming. However once done, this database is enormously flexible with its procedure for querying, enabling small sets of related records to be pulled out easily, even though there may be more than 100,000 records stored. Unfortunately, it does not highlight duplicated records. Exporting the required data as CSV files to DMAP for preparing the maps is relatively straight forward.

The *Bombus* dataset used for this book is approximately 24,000 Watsonian Kent records, allowing for some duplication. Contributors are thanked under Acknowledgements. The records span the timescale from 1837 to 2013, although 68% are from 1980 to 2013.

Notes on the species distribution maps

For mapping, it was decided that the tetrad (2km) scale was best, not least because a significant number of records were only to this resolution.

The date classes of the dots on the species distribution maps represent the most recent record for that 2km square. There may be dots from older date classes for the square which are masked by the more modern one.

Coverage

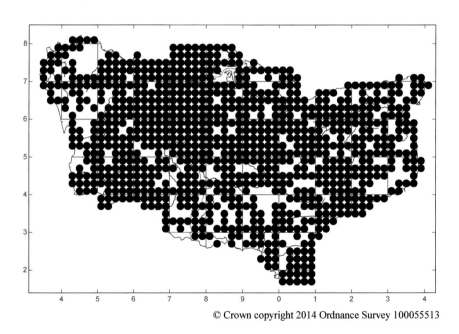

© Crown copyright 2014 Ordnance Survey 100055513

This coverage map shows all locations from where bumblebees have been recorded in Kent. The gaps reflect where the bees have thus far not been found, but may have occurred there and been missed.

Species richness

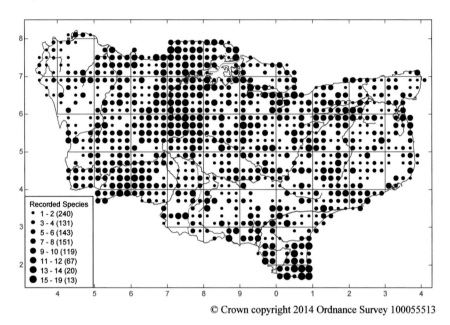

Recorded Species
- 1 - 2 (240)
- 3 - 4 (131)
- 5 - 6 (143)
- 7 - 8 (151)
- 9 - 10 (119)
- 11 - 12 (67)
- 13 - 14 (20)
- 15 - 19 (13)

© Crown copyright 2014 Ordnance Survey 100055513

For the well recorded tetrads, the above map gives a good indication of species richness. However, perhaps eight or so species including cuckoos could be found in most locations, given sufficient recording.

Conservation statuses
Kent statuses

Waite (2000) provided initial county conservation statuses for the Kent flora and fauna. In Allen (2009), for aculeates generally, counting modern tetrad dots on the distribution maps was the key factor for calculating revised Kent conservation statuses. However, bumblebees are strong fliers; the workers can forage some distance from their nests and queens can disperse several kilometres from their maternal nest to found their own colonies (witness the rapid spread of the Tree bumblebee *Bombus hypnorum*). Thus, for bumblebees counting grid squares does not always result in reliable conservation statuses. Given this, considerable redefinition of the Kent conservation categories is carried out here. Unfortunately these categories are not empirical and so are somewhat subjective.

Common:

Here the bumblebee is found widely across the county and usually occurs in gardens where these have good floristic diversity, and in many other habitats. Records are frequently received, sometimes in good numbers.

Kent Scarcity statuses (sometimes labelled RDB4 but here not considered Red listed):

The two categories defined here, **Scarce B** and **Scarce A**, vary mainly in degree, Scarce B being more frequent than Scarce A. In both, the species are still fairly regularly recorded but only in a few habitats, some of which may be subject to fragmentation and degradation. In Scarce B there is not a significant modern decline and hence no predicted danger of the species becoming Red listed. However, in Scarce A, the contained species are thought to be declining and likely to slip into the Red List categories, if present trends continue.

Kent Red Lists (provisional Kent Red Data Book or pKRDB statuses).
Rare (pKRDB3):

A Rare species is one recorded from few habitats, many of which will be subject to fragmentation and degradation, or are in danger of disappearing altogether. The species may also have vanished from former habitats which still exist. Records are still received now but only infrequently. If present trends continue, the species is likely to slip into the Vulnerable category.

Vulnerable (pKRDB2):

In Vulnerable species there may only be one or two remaining habitats, which are in danger of fragmentation and degradation, or disappearing altogether. The species may also have vanished from former habitats which still exist. Few records are now received or there may have only been a handful in the last decade. If present trends continue, the species is likely to slip into the Endangered category.

Endangered (pKRDB1):
To be in the Endangered category, the declining species will survive in only one habitat which itself may not be safe from extinction. Records most probably will not have been received for some time or will number only one or a few in the last decade. If present trends continue, the species is likely to become Extinct.

Critically Endangered (pKRDB1+):
Here the only remaining habitat for the species is virtually non-existent and/or the species has not been recorded for some decades. It may be believed extinct but this is not proven.

Extinct (pKRDB0):
There are no habitats left that this species was known from and/or the species has not been found for many decades, possibly in spite of targeted searches for it. This opinion is based on absence data which can be unreliable but extinction must be beyond reasonable doubt to be placed in this category.

National conservation statuses
National statuses were defined by Shirt (1987) and Falk (1991). Given the enormous changes in range and frequency of many species since, these statuses are considered to be of little value now and we omit them from the species profiles. Biodiversity Action Plan (UK BAP Schedule 41) species statuses are still relevant and where applicable are used.

The IUCN (International Union for the Conservation of Nature) statuses (S.P.M. Roberts, *pers. comm.*) are given here. Internationally, all bumblebees are regarded as being of conservation concern. The Kent IUCN statuses cover the period 1995-2005, whilst those for the UK are for 1995-2006.

Species Quality Scores (SQS)

Species Quality Scores, sometimes called Species Quality Factors, have been defined at the national level by several ecologists for a number of animal groups, mainly for assessing the quality of conservation sites and making comparisons between such sites. There is a good discussion on SQS ratings in a paper by P.H. Williams (2000) using bumblebees as an example, which also points out some of the pitfalls.

♀ *Bombus lapidarius*—Red-tailed bumblebee dusted with pollen © Sarah Seymour

Bombus terrestris—Buff-tailed bumblebee © Sarah Seymour

CHAPTER 4
SUBGENUS AND SPECIES PROFILES

Our use of subgenera

Before presenting detailed profiles of the bumblebees, a consideration of our use of subgenera would be helpful to the reader. A genus contains a group of related species sharply demarked from those in other genera and believed to be all evolutionarily derived from a common, immediate ancestral species. When one studies a particular group, in our case the bumblebee genus *Bombus*, it is frequently observed to be the case that there are groups or clusters of species within a genus where the contained species are very similar to each other structurally and ecologically, but less similar to those in other clusters in the genus. One way of defining or analysing this variation on the common theme has been to describe subgenera, each with its own name, diagnosis and type species (the "subgenerotype"). For example, the subgenus *Bombus (Psithyrus)* contains the cuckoo bumblebees and no other bumblebee species. An alternative is to define these clusters as "species groups". It is generally regarded that the closer two groups of species (or two species) are structurally, the more recently they have become separated in the evolutionary time line. It is possible to reconstruct the putative evolution of the species within a genus, for example, from their common structural features (including their genes) using the methods of cladistics, a fairly recent development in taxonomy (which is the study of the nomenclature and classification of biological organisms).

The subgenera or species groups

The traditional classification (Richards, 1968) placed the world's bumblebees in about 38 subgenera. A simplified classification (Williams *et al.,* 2008) based on an analysis of five genes, listed only 15 subgenera (or species groups of some), formed from the unification of a number of the older ones. Of these 15 subgenera, there are nine found in Britain. These are treated alphabetically in the following pages, with alternative species group names given for those who prefer not to use subgenera.

In the species profiles, it is the British or southern British colour forms which are described. Foreign specimens of species occurring in Britain may vary significantly in colour patterns.

♂ *Bombus terrestris*—Buff-tailed bumblebee © Sarah Seymour

CHAPTER 4   SUBGENUS AND SPECIES PROFILES

Subgenus *Bombus* Latreille, 1802 (*sensu stricto*)
or the *Bombus terrestris* species group

The taxonomic definition of this subgenus remained unchanged in the 1998 revision. The geographical range is Nearctic, Palaearctic and Oriental. There are 17 world species listed on the NHM website.

Many of these species, including all those found in Britain, are black haired, with a yellow collar, a yellow band on T2 and a white or whitish tail.

The British species are *Bombus cryptarum, B. lucorum, B. magnus* and *B. terrestris. B. magnus* has been recorded only once from Kent and is more frequent in the west and north, although it is not an upland species. P.H. Williams (*pers. comm.*) states that although *B. cryptarum* is a good species, it remains poorly characterised and the usual characters given do not work for all specimens. It has been claimed rarely but doubtfully from the county. *B. terrestris* and *B. lucorum* are well known garden species also found in a variety of other habitats.

These bumblebees are pollen storers. They have a short tongue although they can chew holes in the long corolla of many plants to rob the nectar contained within.

Bombus cryptarum (Fabricius, 1775)

It remains unclear if this is a Kentish species; there are no firm records.

P.H. Williams (*pers. comm.*) found a few queens in the *Bombus lucorum* complex (i.e. *B. lucorum*, *B. cryptarum* and *B. magnus*) at Dungeness which on colour pattern characters strongly resembled *B. cryptarum* but with molecular analysis (COI barcoding of mitochondrial DNA) were found to be *B. lucorum*. The workers and males of *B. cryptarum* are virtually indistinguishable from those of *B. lucorum* except by molecular analysis.

It is clear that much further work needs to be done on the complex before even queen specimens can be identified with confidence in the field.

Given the lack of establishment of clear character states, it would be premature to add this species to the Kent list.

♀ *Bombus cryptarum*—a white-tailed bumblebee © Steve Falk

CHAPTER 4   SUBGENUS AND SPECIES PROFILES

♀ *Bombus lucorum*—White-tailed bumblebee © Alan Kenworthy

♂ *Bombus lucorum*—White-tailed bumblebee © Alan Kenworthy

Bombus lucorum (Linnaeus, 1761)   **White-tailed Bumblebee**

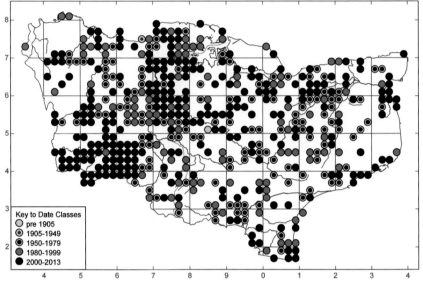

© Crown copyright 2014 Ordnance Survey 100055513

Distribution and Statuses

This is a common and widely distributed bee in Kent with no rarity or scarcity statuses.

Nationally, it is found from the Isles of Scilly east to Kent and north to northern Scotland.

IUCN statuses: Kent Least Concern (LC); UK Least Concern (LC).

Identification and similar species

The queen and worker are black with a lemon yellow collar and band on T2, the tail being pure white. The male is more extensively yellow, with a yellow tuft of hairs on the face, a wide collar and often a band on the rear of the thorax. The yellow on the abdominal segments covers more than T2; T1 and T3 frequently having such bands.

This species can be easily confused with *Bombus terrestris*. However the queens of *B. terrestris* have a buff tail colour and the workers have a thin line of buff hairs above the white tail (but this can fade as the worker becomes sun bleached). It is simpler to distinguish between males of *B. lucorum* and *B. terrestris* as the males of *B. lucorum* have the features said above whereas *B. terrestris* have the colour pattern of the queen and workers of its species.

Bombus soroeensis is a smaller species but could be confused with *B. lucorum*. In this species the yellow band on T2 is narrowed or broken in the middle and creeps onto the rear of T1 at the sides. The tail of this species is variably white or reddish-brown.

The male *Bombus jonellus* might pass for a small *B. lucorum* but has a narrower hind basitarsus.

Autecology
Bombus lucorum is found in a wide range of habitat from gardens, up-lands to woodland edges. Queens are early emergers from February on-wards. The colonies will nest underground in disused rodent holes and on the ground surface under rubble and in cavities. *B. lucorum* is a pollen storer. The colony will live for 3-4 months and there may be two cycles within a year. Colonies can grow to over 200 workers. A short-tongued species which will forage on a wide range of flowers such as white clo-ver, pussy willow, lungwort and will also visit aphids to collect honey-dew.

Predators and parasites
The cuckoo bumblebee *Bombus bohemicus* is a parasite of this species. It has a very limited distribution in Kent.

THE BUMBLEBEES OF KENT

Bombus magnus Vogt, 1911

There is one known Kent specimen of this species, a queen captured near Pen Bars, Dungeness in 1979 by P.H. Williams (*pers. comm.*). Unfortunately this information has come to us too late to produce a distribution map and full species profile.

It is clear this species requires Kent Red List status. It is unlikely to be widespread in the county, the queens being fairly distinct and identifiable by the yellow collar, which is noticeably longer than in *Bombus lucorum* and extends down the sides of the thorax. The workers and males are virtually indistinguishable from those of *B. lucorum* except by molecular analysis.

Bombus magnus is a fairly common species in the West and North but very local in south-east Britain. It is not an upland species, being also found at low elevations.

The only known Kent specimen of *Bombus magnus*—a white-tailed bumblebee, ♀ in the NHM (Natural History Museum, London) collection— leg. P.H. Williams   © Nick Withers

CHAPTER 4   SUBGENUS AND SPECIES PROFILES

♂ *Bombus terrestris*—Buff-tailed bumblebee © Sarah Seymour

Worker *Bombus terrestris*—Buff-tailed bumblebee © Duncan Lawie

Bombus terrestris (Linnaeus, 1758)   **Buff-tailed Bumblebee**

The British form of this bee is *B. terrestris audax* (Harris, 1776).

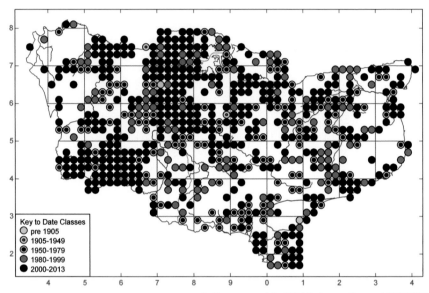

© Crown copyright 2014 Ordnance Survey 100055513

Distribution and Statuses

A very common bee in Kent, widely distributed across the county with no rarity or scarcity statuses.

Common across much of England and Wales, advancing its distribution in Scotland on the east coast.

IUCN statuses: Kent Least Concern (LC); UK Least Concern (LC).

Identification and similar species

The female castes and the male of this bumble are similar, although the queens are larger and generally darker. In this caste, the yellow collar and band on T2 are a darker yellow (compared with *Bombus lucorum*) and the tail is buff or pale brown. The worker has the yellow bands a little lighter and the tail is white usually with a narrow brown band of hair between the black of T3 and the white tail. The male is similar but the amount of brown in the tail is variable.

Bombus terrestris can be confused with *B. lucorum*. The queens are easily distinguished as in *B. terrestris* the tail is buff compared with *B. lucorum* which is pure white. The males can also be easily distinguished because the male of *B. terrestris* is the same colour as the females whereas *B. lucorum* has extra yellow bands and a yellow tuft of hairs on the face. Workers can be hard to distinguish especially when faded. Workers of *B. terrestris* have a thin line of buff hairs above the white tail.

Bombus soroeensis could also be mistaken for *B. terrestris*; however the former species has a broken or narrowed yellow band, interrupted with black hairs, on T2.

Autecology
Bombus terrestris is found in a wide variety of habitats from gardens through to open meadows and woodland edges. The queens are early emergers and during mild winters will emerge or even nest through January. Typically *B. terrestris* nests underground but can be found in blue tit nest boxes, and in loft insulation. The colony cycle will last for 3-4 months. This species can have up to three cycles within one year, something which is rare for our other UK species. It is a pollen storer. This species often has one of the largest worker populations ranging from 200 -400. A short-tongued species, it will forage on white clover, pussy willow, heathers and all species with a short flower corolla. This species will also nectar rob from flowers with long corollas by biting a hole at the base of the corolla where nectar is produced and inserting its shorter tongue. The hole then allows other shorter tongued bees such as short-tongued bumblebees and honeybees to also nectar rob. New queens mate on the soil/ground surface or on flower heads.

THE BUMBLEBEES OF KENT

Predators and parasites

The cuckoo bumblebee *Bombus vestalis*, common across the county, is a parasite of this species. In Greece and on the Mediterranean island of Corsica, the non-British *B. perezi* (Schulthess-Rechberg, 1886) is also a parasite.

♀ *Bombus terrestris*—Buff-tailed bumblebee © Nikki Gammans

CHAPTER 4   SUBGENUS AND SPECIES PROFILES

Subgenus *Cullumanobombus* Vogt, 1911
or the *Bombus cullumanus* species group

This subgenus has been enlarged by the unification of 11 of the former subgenera and hence contains 23 world species. The distribution is Neotropical, Nearctic and Palaearctic. The Nearctic and Palaearctic species are mainly grassland specialists whilst those of the Neotropical tend to be montane (Williams *et al*, 2014)

Only one species has been recorded from the UK and Europe, *Bombus cullumanus*. The dark colour form of this bee, once found in Britain and north-western Europe, has undergone a catastrophic decline and is now apparently extinct. Other colour forms further afield are still common, e.g. on the steppes of Asia (Williams, *pers. comm.*).

Bombus cullumanus was last recorded from the UK in 1941.

Side view of a pinned ♀ *Bombus cullumanus*—Cullum's bumblebee in the collection of the NHM (Natural History Museum, London) © Nick Withers

Bombus cullumanus (Kirby, 1802)   **Cullum's Bumblebee**

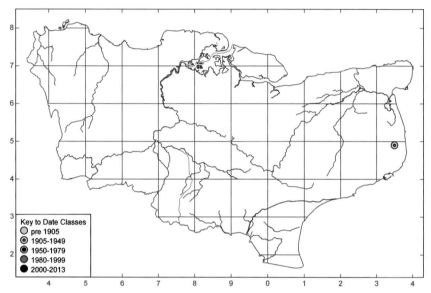

© Crown copyright 2014 Ordnance Survey 100055513

Distribution and Statuses

This bee is extinct in Kent and the UK. There is only one known Kent record, from 1911. It was known from calcareous grassland in the south-east of Britain.

Kent status: Extinct

IUCN Statuses: Kent Extinct (RE); UK Extinct (RE).

Identification and similar species

Bombus cullumanus queens and workers are black haired, sometimes with a faint trace of a yellow collar and fringe at the rear of the thorax, and a red tail. The male is more extensively yellow with a broad yellow collar, a band at the rear of the thorax and a yellow band on T2. In the south of its European range the female castes resemble the male description given here.

Superficially similar species are *Bombus lapidarius*, *B. ruderarius* and in the male, *B. monticola* and *B. pratorum*. Given the unlikely event of it being recorded in Kent again, no detailed comparison with other species needs to be given.

Autecology

Bombus cullumanus was associated with flower rich calcareous grasslands. This species is a late emerger, from May onwards. It nests underground in disused rodent nest sites. This bee has a short tongue, particularly foraging on leguminous plants such as white clover, and knapweeds and thistles (noted from where it still exists).

Predators and parasites

There are no recorded cuckoo species for this bee.

Pinned ♀ *Bombus cullumanus*—Cullum's bumblebee, in the collection of the NHM
© Nick Withers

Subgenus *Kallobombus* Dalla Torre, 1880
or the *Bombus soroeensis* species group

This subgenus is monotypic, i.e. has only one species. Its range is west Palaearctic, east to northern China.

The only species, *Bombus soroeensis*, superficially resembles *Bombus (Bombus)* species. It is separated by not having a preapical notch and "oblique groove" in the mandible.

The main habitat across much of the range is flower rich grassland.

Bombus soroeensis (Fabricius, 1776)   Broken-belted Bumblebee

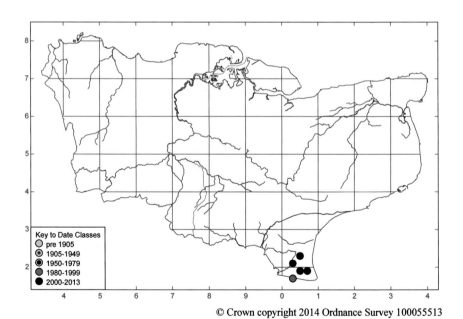

© Crown copyright 2014 Ordnance Survey 100055513

Distribution and Statuses
It has a very limited range in Kent, only found locally and sporadically

on Romney Marsh. It is more frequent in the west and north of the UK.

Kent status: Vulnerable.

IUCN statuses: Kent Vulnerable (VU); UK Near Threatened (NT).

Identification and similar species
This bee is black haired with a yellow collar and a band, narrowed or often broken, on T2. The tail is whitish in the female castes. The male is similar to the females but usually has reddish-brown in the tail.

This species can be confused with *Bombus lucorum* and *B. terrestris*. The most notable difference is in T2 where black hairs are present in a break or narrowing in the middle of the band. This species also tends to be smaller than *B. terrestris* and *B. lucorum*. It can further be separated from these species by the lack of a preapical notch and oblique groove in the mandible.

Autecology
Found in flower rich grasslands, heathland, uplands and moorland, there being recent records from the Dungeness area in the south of Kent. It is a late emerging species from June onwards. Colonies are pollen storers and nest underground. This species forms a small colony size of up to 100 workers. It is a short-tongued species which feeds on legumes. Males may begin to fly in September/October,

Predators and parasites
There are no recorded cuckoo species on this bee in the UK. In continental Europe the non-British *Bombus quadricolor* (Lepeletier, 1832) is a parasite.

THE BUMBLEBEES OF KENT

Pinned ♀ *Bombus soroeensis*—Broken-belted bumblebee, in the
NHM collection © Nick Withers

♂ *Bombus soroeensis*—Broken-belted bumblebee
© Nick Owen

CHAPTER 4   SUBGENUS AND SPECIES PROFILES

Subgenus *Megabombus* Dalla Torre, 1880
or the *Bombus argillaceus* species group

This subgenus as now conceived is formed from the unification of three former subgenera and contains 20 world species. The range is mainly Oriental but also Palaearctic.

Two species are known from Britain, *Bombus hortorum* and *B. ruderatus*. These are closely related and similar in appearance. They are black haired with a yellow collar and band at the rear of the thorax, a band on T1 and a white tail. Partial melanism is known in both species, although more frequent in *B. ruderatus*. This species is sometimes all black, including the tail.

The subgenerotype, *Bombus argillaceus* (Scopoli, 1763), is often similar in colour to the British species, although the queens sometimes have yellow bands at the front and back of the thorax, and an all black-haired gaster. The distribution of *B. argillaceus* is mainly in south and southeast Europe, including the Balkans, east to Kazakhstan. It is found in the French, Italian, Swiss and Austrian Alps, Hungary and parts of Romania.

These bees have a long face and very long tongue, usually visiting flowers with a long corolla, such as *Digitalis* and *Trifolium*. They are effective pollinators of several cultivated cattle and sheep fodder plants. They are pocket makers.

Bombus hortorum is a well known garden species, as its vernacular name of Garden Bumblebee suggests; however it also occurs in many other habitats. *B. ruderatus* has a much declined distribution and is mainly coastal in Kent.

THE BUMBLEBEES OF KENT

Bombus hortorum (Linnaeus, 1758)   **Garden Bumblebee**

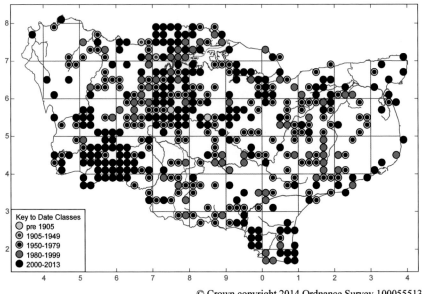

© Crown copyright 2014 Ordnance Survey 100055513

Distribution and Statuses

This is a common bee distributed across the county, with no rarity or scarcity statuses.

Nationally, found from the Isles of Scilly and Cornwall to Kent and north to Orkney.

IUCN statuses: Kent Least Concern (LC); UK Least Concern (LC).

Identification and similar species

The two female castes and the male of this bee are black with yellow bands on the front and back of the thorax, and a yellow band on T1. The hind thoracic band is always narrower than that at the front. The tail is white. In melanistic specimens the yellow bands on the thorax and abdomen are faded but the tail colour always remains white, at least at the tips of the tail hairs. The bees have a very long narrow head and long tongue, the longest of any British bumblebee.

Similar species are *Bombus ruderatus* and, superficially, *B. jonellus*. *B. hortorum* is a smaller species than *B. ruderatus*. In the fully striped form, the second thoracic band is always narrower than the first in *B. hortorum*. In melanistic specimens the tail of *B. hortorum* remains white as the yellow bands fade. In *B. ruderatus* the second thoracic band is always the same width as the front one and the tail fades to black in melanistic cases.

Bombus jonellus could possibly be confused with *B. hortorum* as it has similar bands across all sections of the body. However, *B. jonellus* is a smaller species than *B. hortorum* and has a much shorter face (as wide as long) compared to *B. hortorum* which has a very long, narrow face.

Autecology

It is found in various habitats including gardens and open flower rich meadows. Queens emerge from hibernation March-April and are classed as early emergers. This species forms underground nests, most likely in old rodent holes. The colonies will live for 3-4 months and there will normally be two cycles within a year. *Bombus hortorum* is a pocket maker. In UK populations, nests are usually small, with 30-120 workers. This is a long-tongued species and can be found foraging on foxgloves, red clover and field beans. It forages on species with long corollas. Queens and males will mate on flower heads.

Predators and parasites

Bombus hortorum is the principal host of the cuckoo *B. barbutellus* which appears to have drastically declined in the county.

THE BUMBLEBEES OF KENT

♀ *Bombus hortorum*—Garden bumblebee
© Alan Kenworthy

♂ *Bombus hortorum*—Garden bumblebee © Steve Falk

CHAPTER 4   SUBGENUS AND SPECIES PROFILES

Light form ♂ *Bombus ruderatus*—Ruderal bumblebee
© Nikki Gammans

Intermediate form ♀ *Bombus ruderatus*—Ruderal bumblebee © Duncan Lawie

Melanistic ♂ *Bombus ruderatus* (= var. *perniger*) — Ruderal bumblebee © Sarah Seymour

THE BUMBLEBEES OF KENT

Bombus ruderatus (Fabricius, 1775)   **Ruderal Bumblebee**

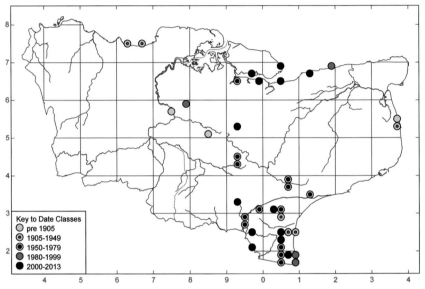

© Crown copyright 2014 Ordnance Survey 100055513

Distribution and Statuses
A bee that has declined considerably in the county, known only from the Swale marshes and Romney/Walland Marshes at present. Possibly making a small recovery in numbers.

Nationally, a local and declined bee; found from Cornwall to Kent and north to Lincolnshire.

Kent status: Vulnerable.   National status: UK BAP Priority Species.

IUCN statuses: Kent Endangered (EN); UK Vulnerable (VU).

Identification and similar species
This bee, in its lighter forms, has three yellow bands, at the front and rear of the thorax and on T1. The front and rear thoracic bands are always of

the same width. It is prone to melanism however, and dark, even all black, forms are found. Intermediate colour forms are found; as the bands of the thorax begin to reduce in size the tail colour becomes more black. The front band, however, always remains the same width as the rear one. The black form has been called *Bombus ruderatus* var. *perniger* (Harris, 1776) = var. *harrisellus* (Kirby, 1802). The face of the bee is very long and it has a long tongue.

This bee closely resembles *Bombus hortorum* and to a lesser extent, *B. jonellus*. The queens of *B. ruderatus* are distinctly larger than those of *B. hortorum* and tend to be darker. The other main distinguishing features are the thoracic bands are always the same width (through all intermediate forms) and as the bee becomes more melanistic the tail fades to black whilst that of *B. hortorum* stays white. The workers are sometimes very similar, requiring careful examination. *B. ruderatus* has a long face and tongue similar to *B. hortorum*. *B. jonellus* could also possibly be confused but as with *B. hortorum* the second band on the thorax is narrower than the first.

The darker forms of *Bombus ruderatus* resemble *B. subterraneus* but have the distinctly longer face. *B. ruderatus* also has ginger hairs around the mandibles (visible with a hand lens). The hair is also much shorter in *B. subterraneus*.

Autecology

It is found in open, flower-rich meadows and is a late emerging species appearing from May onwards. It nests underground in old, disused rodent holes. The colony cycle lasts for 3-4 months with one cycle per year. *Bombus ruderatus* forms colonies of up to 150 workers. It is a long -tongued species foraging on red clover, vetches, white dead nettle, comfrey and lavender. Males will congregate around suitable forage, feeding and looking for queens to mate with.

Predators and parasites

The cuckoo *Bombus barbutellus* may parasitise this species, as well as *B. hortorum*. On the Mediterranean island of Corsica, the non-British *B. maxillosus* (Klug, 1817) is a parasite of *B. ruderatus*.

♀ *Bombus lapidarius*—Red-tailed bumblebee © Nick Withers

CHAPTER 4   SUBGENUS AND SPECIES PROFILES

Subgenus *Melanobombus* Dalla Torre, 1880
or the *B. lapidarius* species group

Melanobombus, in its modern usage, was formed from the unification of three former subgenera and as such contains 16 world species. The distribution is Palaearctic but mainly Oriental.

There is only one British species in this subgenus, also found in Kent, *Bombus lapidarius*. It is a quite distinctive bee with its black body and bright red tail in the female castes.

This is a fairly short-tongued bumblebee which forages on a wide variety of host plants with a short to medium length corolla, including rosaceous fruit trees and Asteraceae. It is a pollen storer.

♂ *Bombus lapidarius*– Red-tailed bumblebee © Duncan Lawie

Bombus lapidarius (Linnaeus, 1758)   **Red-tailed Bumblebee**

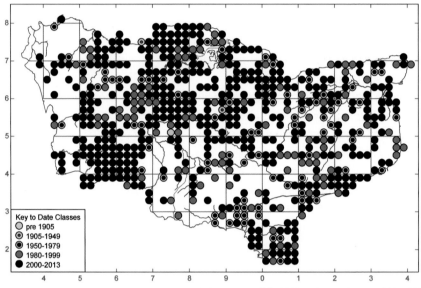

© Crown copyright 2014 Ordnance Survey 100055513

Distribution and Statuses

This is a common and widely distributed bumblebee in the county. It is said to do well in exposed situations and so is well represented on the coast. It has no county statuses.

Nationally, this is a common species in the south, found as far north as northern Scotland, but not to the Orkneys.

IUCN statuses: Kent Least Concern (LC); UK Least Concern (LC).

Identification and similar species

Bombus lapidarius is a distinctive bee. The female castes are generally large with the body hairs black, apart from a bright red tail. The corbicular hair fringe is black. The male has a prominent yellow band on the front of the thorax and rarely one on the gaster (abdomen), with a bright red tail. There is a tuft of yellow hairs on the face.

Similar species include *Bombus ruderarius* and the workerless cuckoo species of *B. lapidarius*, *B. rupestris*. In comparison to *B. lapidarius*, *B. ruderarius* has the corbicular hair fringe with mainly red hairs, which can be seen with low magnification. The giz of the bee is also different, being a smaller, more round looking bee, with the tail colour more ginger than the bright red of *B. lapidarius*. The males are easily distinguishable as the male *B. ruderarius* does not have the tuft of yellow hairs on the face and the yellow bands on the thorax and gaster are rather dull and suffused. *B. rupestris* is very similar in the female caste but it has very darkened wing membranes and no pollen baskets, as it is a cuckoo species. Males are not easily confused as those of *B. rupestris* lacking the yellow hair tuft.

The male *Bombus lapidarius* is sometimes confused with the non-Kentish *B. monticola* and that of the smaller *B. pratorum*. *B. monticola* is found at elevations greater than 300m and has a more extensively red abdomen compared to the red tail of *B. lapidarius*. The male of *B. lapidarius* has much less yellow on the gaster than *B. pratorum*.

The extinct species *Bombus cullumanus* and *B. pomorum* also bore resemblances to *B. lapidarius* but need not be discussed further here.

Autecology
Bombus lapidarius is a generalist found in habitats from woodland edge to gardens. An early emerging bumblebee from February to April. Will nest underground in disused rodent holes and has occasionally been found in tit nest boxes. Colonies last for 3-4 months and they grow to about 150 workers. Normally there are two colony cycles per year. Queens will hibernate under tree roots in north facing aspects. *B. lapidarius* has a middle length tongue and will forage on a wide variety of

flowers white clover, birds foot trefoil, dandelions and pussy willow. Males patrol individual circuits in areas where queens are likely to be.

Predators and parasites
Bombus lapidarius is the usual host of *B. rupestris*. The queens of this bee are sometimes predated by great tits *Parus major*.

Subgenus *Psithyrus* Lepeletier, 1833
or the *Bombus rupestris* species group

This subgenus is found in the Nearctic, Palaearctic and Oriental regions, and has 27-29 world species. There are six British and Kent species.

Bombus (Psithyrus) comprises the cuckoo bumblebees, which are nest parasites of the "social" *Bombus*. They are characterised by the females (there are no workers) not having pollen baskets and with a thin coat of body hairs, both adaptations unsuitable for collecting and carrying pollen.

The amount of information available on the various cuckoo species is very variable and a complete list of confirmed hosts for each species is still lacking.

It is often said that the cuckoo resembles its main host in the similar colour of the coat. This is true of *Bombus rupestris* and its hosts, *B. lapidarius* and the non-British *B. sichelii* Radoszkowski, 1860. However, the case is not so clear in other European species and is not shown in those of the Nearctic. Where it is found, it does not dupe the host workers, which identify nest mates by the colony scent but may serve to inform vertebrate predators, which then have one less aposematic colour pattern to learn. Hence, this may be Mullerian mimicry. An analysis of known parasite and host colour patterns is given in Williams (2008).

A common observation in the field is that the female cuckoos have a deeper, softer buzz than that of the true females and this is sometimes a good giz character for picking them out in flight. However, the males can be found quite easily congregating on flower heads in the late summer.

A structure common to the females of the cuckoos, not present in the "true" species, is found on sternum 6 (S6). There are a pair of raised bumps (called callosities) which can join to form a "U" shape. The function of these may be to help protect the vulnerable sting area of the cuckoo, so that it cannot easily be disarmed by the host workers in combat.

Callosities on S6 of ♀ *Bombus barbutellus*—
Barbut's cuckoo bee © Steve Falk

THE BUMBLEBEES OF KENT

Bombus barbutellus (Kirby, 1802)   **Barbut's Cuckoo Bee**

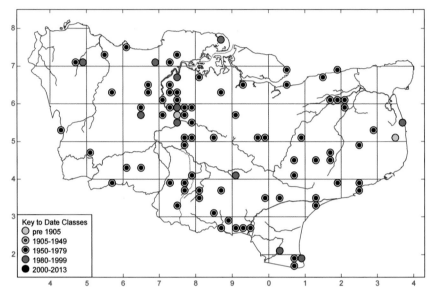

© Crown copyright 2014 Ordnance Survey 100055513

Distribution and Statuses

This was once a widely distributed and fairly common species in the county but has declined considerably, to the point where no new records are being made, the last being in 1988.

Nationally, the decline is not so pronounced and therefore there is no national status.

Kent status: Vulnerable.

IUCN statuses: Kent Endangered (EN); UK Least Concern (LC).

Identification and similar species

This species generally resembles its usual host, *B. hortorum*, being black haired with yellow bands on the front and rear of the thorax, sometimes one on the gaster and a white tail. However the coat is much thinner and the female lacks the pollen baskets.

Bombus sylvestris and to a lesser extent *B. campestris* are cuckoos which resemble *B. barbutellus*. However, the male of *B. sylvestris* has the terminal segment of the gaster black with a tip of reddish hairs whereas in *B. barbutellus* the hairs are white. The female *B. sylvestris* has black hairs at the tip of the abdomen whereas again *B. barbutellus* is white. *B. campestris* has a light form similar to that of *B. barbutellus* but the tail is generally more yellow or discoloured as opposed to white.

Autecology
It is found in nests of *Bombus hortorum* and *B. ruderatus* which are underground. Emerges from hibernation April onwards. As with all cuckoo species it is short-tongued. It will feed on a range of flowers such as brambles, thistles and white clover. As a parasitic bumblebee it does not collect pollen. Males patrol areas with scent markings.

Predators and parasites
There are no known parasites or predators on this species.

♀ *Bombus barbutellus*– Barbut's cuckoo bee © Nick Owen

♂ *Bombus barbutellus*– Barbut's cuckoo bee © Nick Owen

Bombus bohemicus (Seidl, 1837)   **Gypsy Cuckoo Bee**

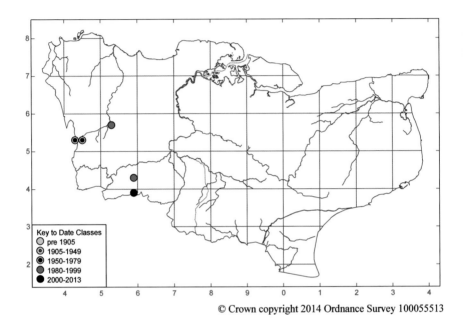

Distribution and Statuses

Although common in the west and north of Britain, this is a rare species in Kent, found only in the west and south-west of the county.

Kent status: Vulnerable.

IUCN statuses: Kent Vulnerable (VU); UK Least Concern (LC).

Identification and similar species

This species bears a strong resemblance to the southern *Bombus vestalis* except in the paler lemon yellow markings. Both sexes of *B. bohemicus* are largely black with a lemon yellow band on the front of the thorax, sometimes one at the rear, one on the front of the gaster and pale yellow side spots on the gaster between the black and the white tail. The hair length of *B. bohemicus* tends to be the longer than the other UK cuckoo species and this can be used to distinguish it from other cuckoo species. Sun-bleached specimens can only be separated on structural characters from *B. vestalis*, including antennal segment lengths in the male and the shape of the callosities (bumps) on the underside of the female 6th abdominal segment.

Autecology

A cuckoo bumblebee which parasitises *Bombus lucorum* and emerges from hibernation in April. It has a short tongue and visits white clover, thistles and a wide variety of flowers, but does not collect pollen. Males patrol scent marked areas looking for females.

Predators and parasites

There are no known parasites or predators on this species.

♂ *Bombus bohemicus*—Gypsy cuckoo bee © Nick Owen

♀ *Bombus bohemicus*—Gypsy cuckoo bee © Nick Owen

Bombus campestris (Panzer, 1800)   **Field Cuckoo Bee**

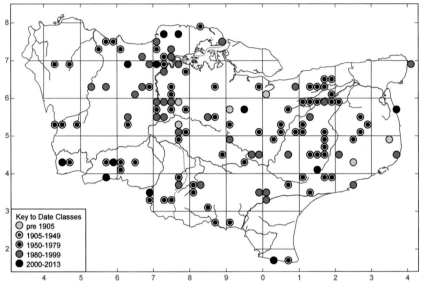

© Crown copyright 2014 Ordnance Survey 100055513

Distribution and Statuses

This was formerly a widespread species in the county but declined considerably in the 1970s. It is now scarce in Kent, although reported to be increasing in some other southern counties.

Kent status: Vulnerable.

IUCN statuses: Kent Vulnerable (VU); UK Least Concern (LC).

Identification and similar species

This is a distinctive species, prone to melanism. The lighter forms have yellow bands at the front and back of the thorax, and a yellowish tail. The tail of the male abrades to form paired tufts on segments T4-T6. Dark forms are frequent and an all black cuckoo is likely to be this species.

The yellow-tailed form of male *Bombus sylvestris* looks very similar to this species but has the reddish hairs at the tip of the gaster as opposed to yellow in this species.

Autecology
It most likely parasitises all carder bees (*Bombus muscorum, B. humilis, B. pascuorum, B. ruderarius* and *B. sylvarum*). It emerges from April onwards and finds nests on the ground surface where carder bees nest. Occurring in a wide variety of habitats, it visits a wide assortment of flowers for nectar such as white clover, thistles etc.

Predators and parasites
There are no known predators or parasites of this species.

♀ *Bombus campestris*—Field cuckoo bee © Steve Falk

Light form ♂ *Bombus campestris* – Field cuckoo bee © Steve Falk

Dark form ♂ *Bombus campestris*— Field cuckoo bee © Jeremy Early

Bombus rupestris (Fabricius, 1793)   Hill Cuckoo Bee

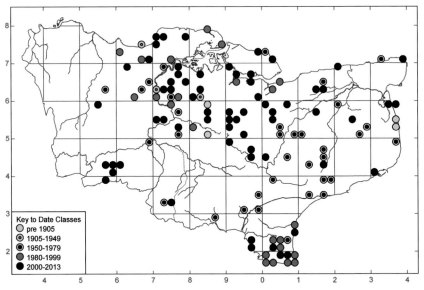

© Crown copyright 2014 Ordnance Survey 100055513

Distribution and Statuses
Now widely distributed across the county, this species became very rare in the 1950s-80s in Kent.

Nationally, this species occurs from Cornwall to Kent and north to Northumbria.

Kent status: No status.

IUCN statuses: Kent Least Concern (LC); UK Least Concern (LC).

Identification and similar species
This is a large black species with a red tail, the male having faint greyish bands on the front of the thorax and on the gaster. The female closely

100

resembles the queen of *Bombus lapidarius* but has the wing membranes much darker and does not have pollen baskets. Males of *B. ruderarius* may be confused with the males of *B. rupestris*. The latter has grey bands on the thorax but these also extend to the abdomen, where in *B. ruderarius* the grey hairs only occur on the thorax. There are no other cuckoos which resemble this species.

Autecology
It is common in gardens and found in a wide variety of other habitats, as does its host *Bombus lapidarius*. It emerges from hibernation March-April. There is one colony cycle per year inside a *B. lapidarius* nest. It is a short-tongued bumblebee which visits white clover, bramble and similar species to *B. lapidarius*. Males and females will often congregate on open headed flowers.

Predators and parasites
There are no known predators or parasites of this species.

♀ *Bombus rupestris*– Hill cuckoo bee
© Jeremy Early

♂ *Bombus rupestris*– Hill cuckoo bee
© Steve Falk

Bombus sylvestris (Lepeletier, 1833)   **Forest Cuckoo Bee**

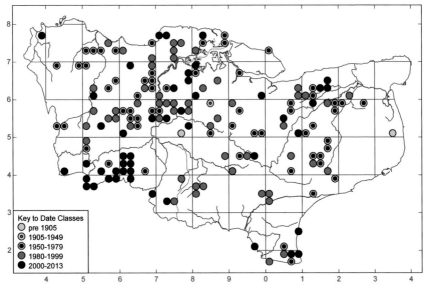

© Crown copyright 2014 Ordnance Survey 100055513

Distribution and Statuses

This is a widely distributed and common species in the county, possibly showing signs of a modern decline.

Nationally, it occurs from Cornwall to Kent and to northern Scotland.

IUCN statuses: Kent Least Concern (LC); UK Least Concern (LC).

Identification and similar species

This is a medium sized species with a black coat, a yellow band on the front of the thorax and a white tail. T6, or T7 in the male, is black haired with reddish hairs at the very tip. A form of the male has a yellowish

102

rather than a white tail.

Bombus barbutellus can be confused with *B. sylvestris* but it does not have the reddish hairs at the tip of the gaster and has less black hairs on T6, or T7 in the male.

Autecology

Bombus sylvestris parasitises nests of *B. pratorum*, *B. monticola* and *B. jonellus* and emerges from hibernation from April onwards. This is a short-tongued parasitic bumblebee which visits a wide range of flowers like the hosts. Males patrol scent marked areas looking for females. The males are the first to appear of all the cuckoos.

Predators and parasites

There are no known predators or parasites of this species.

♂ *Bombus sylvestris*– Forest cuckoo bee, showing the red hairs at the very tip of the gaster
© Nick Owen

THE BUMBLEBEES OF KENT

♀ *Bombus sylvestris*—Forest cuckoo bee © Nick Owen

Yellow-tailed form of ♂ *Bombus sylvestris*—Forest cuckoo bee © Louise Hislop

CHAPTER 4 SUBGENUS AND SPECIES PROFILES

White-tailed form of ♂ *Bombus sylvestris*—Forest cuckoo bee ©
Steve Falk

♀ *Bombus vestalis*—Vestal cuckoo bee © Nikki Gammans

***Bombus vestalis* (Geoffroy in Fourcroy, 1785) Vestal Cuckoo Bee**

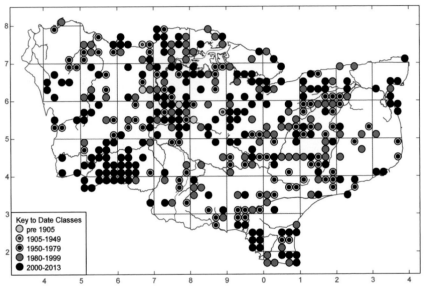

© Crown copyright 2014 Ordnance Survey 100055513

Distribution and Statuses
This is a common and widely distributed species in Kent.

Nationally, distributed from the Isles of Scilly to Kent and north to the Central Lowlands of Scotland.

IUCN statuses: Kent Least Concern (LC); UK Least Concern (LC).

Identification and similar species
This is a large black haired species. There is a darkish yellow band on the front of the thorax and yellow side patches between the black of the abdomen and the white tail. T6 in the female is largely black.

It bears a strong resemblance to *Bombus bohemicus* and where both species occur together, sun-bleached specimens may need to be microscopi-

106

cally examined for critical identification. However, *B. vestalis* has shorter hair in comparison.

Autecology
It is abundant in gardens and found in a wide variety of other habitats like its host *Bombus terrestris*. Females emerge from hibernation from April onwards. It will visit a wide range of flowers such as bramble, thistles etc. Males patrol scent marked areas.

Predators and parasites
There are no known predators or parasites of this species.

♂ *Bombus vestalis*—Vestal cuckoo bee © Sarah Seymour

THE BUMBLEBEES OF KENT

Subgenus *Pyrobombus* Dalla Torre, 1880
or the *Bombus hypnorum* species group

This subgenus is widely distributed in the Nearctic and Palaearctic regions. Also found in the Oriental region and on some oceanic islands.

It is formed from the unification of two of the former subgenera and contains 51 world species, making it the largest subgenus in *Bombus*. Often the species have some reddish hairs, usually on the gaster. Many of the species are found in northerly or upland locations, *B. monticola* being an example.

There are four British species: *Bombus hypnorum, B. jonellus, B. monticola* and *B. pratorum*. These are all found in Kent apart from *B. monticola*.

These are short-tongued bumblebees and some species frequently forage on Rosaceae, such as *Cotoneaster* and *Rubus*. They are pollen storers.

Worker *Bombus hypnorum*—Tree bumblebee
© Alan Kenworthy

CHAPTER 4   SUBGENUS AND SPECIES PROFILES

Bombus monticola Smith, F., 1849　　　　**Blaeberry Bumblebee**

There are occasional, erroneous *Bombus monticola* records for Kent. It is a rare upland species found in the hills of south-west England, Wales, northern England and Scotland, and is declining where still found. It is recorded at elevations greater than 300m. The few Kent vouchers (usually photographs) we have examined have proved to be males of either *B. lapidarius* or *B. pratorum*. Please see the descriptions of those species to avoid confusion.

♀ *Bombus monticola*—Blaeberry bumblebee © Dave Goulson

Bombus hypnorum (Linnaeus, 1758)   **Tree Bumblebee**

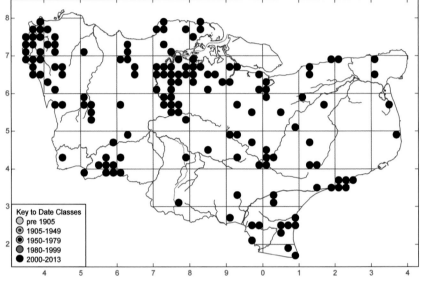

© Crown copyright 2014 Ordnance Survey 100055513

Distribution and Statuses

This bee has recently colonised the UK. It was first found near South-ampton in 2001 and in Kent in 2006. It has spread rapidly across southern Britain and north as far as the Central Lowlands of Scotland.

Kent status: No status.

IUCN statuses: Kent ABSENT; UK Least Concern (LC).

Identification and similar species

This is a distinctive species which could possibly be confused with some of the carder bees. It has a reddish brown haired thorax and a black gaster with a white tail in all of the female castes and the male. This combination of colour characteristics makes it unique in the British fauna. Occasionally, melanistic specimens are found which still have some reddish-brown on the thorax and a white tail. In some specimens there may also be a brown band on T1 of the abdomen. It may be confused with *Bombus pascuorum* but the latter has a ginger tail as opposed to the white of *B. hypnorum*.

Autecology

It is found in a wide variety of habitats including gardens. Queens emerge from March-April. It nests in old woodpecker holes and is very commonly found in tit nest boxes and loft insulation. Queens appear to be very opportunistic in their nest choices. Colonies live for 3-4 months. There are two colony cycles per year but some areas of the UK (particularly the South) could potentially have three. Workers in a nest are thought to number between 150-250. It is a short-tongued bumblebee which forages on white clover and many garden plants. Males 'nest entrance gather' trying to enter a colony to mate with the new queens; guard workers often deter them. Once a queen leaves the nest a male lands on her back and they fall to the ground to mate.

Predators and parasites

Bombus hypnorum could possibly be a host of *Bombus sylvestris*. In continental Europe the non-British *Bombus norvegicus* (Sparre-Schneider, 1918) is a cuckoo on this species, as is the UK species *B. barbutellus*.

THE BUMBLEBEES OF KENT

♂ *Bombus hypnorum*—Tree bumblebee
© Alan Kenworthy

Worker *Bombus hypnorum*—Tree bumblebee,
with white pollen in corbicula © Nick Withers

♂ *Bombus jonellus*—Heath bumblebee © Nikki Gammans

Worker *Bombus jonellus*—Heath bumblebee © Nick Owen

THE BUMBLEBEES OF KENT

Bombus jonellus (Kirby, 1802)   **Heath Bumblebee**

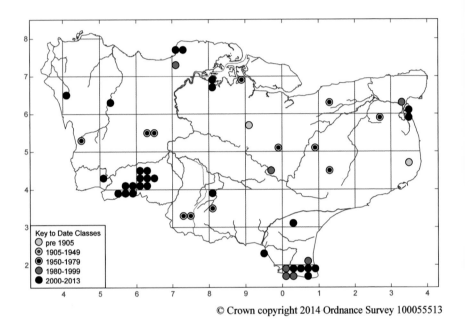

© Crown copyright 2014 Ordnance Survey 100055513

Distribution and Statuses
This species is widely distributed but scarce in Kent. It occurs mainly on heathland but is also coastal in the county.

It is found from the Isles of Scilly to Kent and north to the Shetlands.

Kent status: Scarce B.

IUCN statuses: Kent Near Threatened (NT); UK Least Concern (LC).

Identification and similar species
This is a black-haired species with yellow bands at the front and rear of the thorax and on the gaster, and a white tail in the two female castes and

the male. The yellow band at the front of the thorax is wider than that at the rear. Occasionally, melanistic specimens occur.

It is most easily confused with *Bombus hortorum* but *B. jonellus* has a face as wide as long, compared to the long face of *B. hortorum*. The male could possibly be overlooked as a small *B. lucorum* but the hair is longer in *B. jonellus*.

Autecology
This species has always been associated with heathland; however, is found in hay meadows and a variety of coastal habitats. Queens emerge in March and the species may have two colony cycles within a year in the south of England. The nest will be formed below the ground surface but can be seen on the ground surface in rubble and cavities. It is thought to nest in wetter areas. It is a pollen storer with small colony size of under 100 and is a short-medium tongued bee which will feed on red clover, bramble and legumes. On heathland it is often recorded foraging on *Calluna* and *Erica*.

Predators and parasites
Bombus jonellus is a host of *B. sylvestris*. In continental Europe the non-British *B. flavidus* Eversmann, 1852 is also a parasite.

Bombus pratorum (Linnaeus, 1761)   **Early Bumblebee**

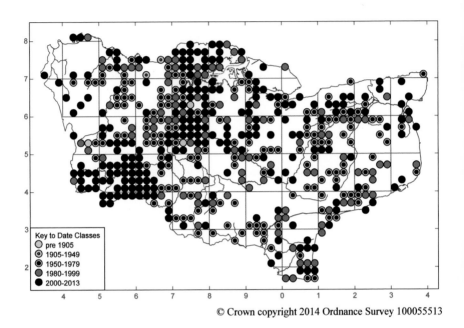

© Crown copyright 2014 Ordnance Survey 100055513

Distribution and Statuses
This is a common and widely distributed species across the county.

Nationally, it occurs from the Isles of Scilly to Kent and to northern Scotland, but not as far as the Northern Isles.

IUCN statuses: Kent Least Concern (LC); UK Least Concern (LC).

Identification and similar species
This is a medium sized, black haired species, the queens and workers with a yellow band on the front of the thorax, and one on T2 and a ginger -reddish tail (in some workers the band on T2 can be missing). The male

is similar but fluffier, with much more yellow banding and a yellow hair tuft on the face.

The female castes are distinctive but the male, with its extensive yellow banding, could be confused with the non-Kentish *Bombus monticola* or as a small *B. lapidarius*. In contrast to the latter *B. pratorum* males have a yellow band on T2 of the abdomen. In *B. monticola* the red extends over much of the abdomen compared to just the red tail of *B. pratorum*. Also, it is found at elevations of over 300m.

Autecology
Commonly found in gardens and a wide variety of other habitats. Queens begin to emerge from March onwards and there are two colony cycles in the south of England. It is an underground nester in old rodents holes and may nest on the ground surface under rubble or debris. The colony cycle lasts for 3-4 months and colonies are small with under 100 workers. The species is a pollen storer and short-tongued, visiting a wide variety of flowers in gardens such as lavender, sweet peas, bramble etc. Males will nectar on flowers and await queens for mating.

Predators and parasites
Bombus pratorum is a confirmed host of *B. sylvestris* and *B. campestris*.

THE BUMBLEBEES OF KENT

♂ *Bombus pratorum*—Early bumblebee © Alan Kenworthy

♀ *Bombus pratorum*—Early bumblebee © Steve Falk

CHAPTER 4   SUBGENUS AND SPECIES PROFILES

Subgenus *Subterraneobombus* Vogt, 1911
or the *Bombus subterraneus* species group

The taxonomy of this subgenus remained unchanged in the 2008 revision. It is related to *Megabombus*.

This subgenus is Nearctic, Palaearctic and Oriental in range, with 11 world species. Two species are recorded from Britain, *Bombus distinguendus* and *B. subterraneus*. Both species have experienced serious decline in the UK, indeed *B. subterraneus* being declared extinct in 2000, with no UK records since 1988.

Bombus distinguendus declined much earlier than *B. subterraneus*, the last known Kent record being in 1900. It has retreated to the very north of Scotland, some of the Western Isles and Orkney, where it survives on coastal machair grassland sites. *B. subterraneus* was last found in the UK at Dungeness, Kent, where it had a stronghold for a number of years.

These are long-tongued species which are effective pollinators of cattle fodder legumes. This is the reason *Bombus subterraneus* was taken to New Zealand, to pollinate Red clover *Trifolium pratense*. The species are pocket makers.

Bombus subterraneus was particularly late to emerge in the spring, often not being found till the end of May or beginning of June. This is perhaps the reason for its short coat of hairs; appearing so late it did not need a dense coat. Due to its late appearance it was particularly vulnerable to the loss of flower-rich meadows.

THE BUMBLEBEES OF KENT

Bombus distinguendus **Morawitz, 1869**   **Great Yellow Bumblebee**

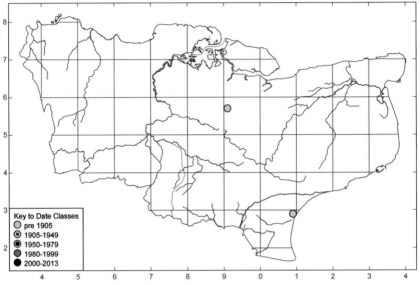

© Crown copyright 2014 Ordnance Survey 100055513

Distribution and Statuses

This was always a local species in Kent but probably became extinct in the county in the early 1900s.

It has retreated northwards to northern Scotland and some of the islands in modern times.

Kent status: Extinct.   National status: UK BAP Priority Species.

IUCN statuses: Kent Extinct (RE); UK Critically Endangered (CR).

Identification and similar species

In the female castes this bee is unmistakable; it is a large, yellow haired bee with a black stripe between the wing bases. The male is similar, but could be confused with that of *Bombus subterraneus*, which also has extensive yellow hairs, at least on the gaster. However these species are geographically separated, with *B. distinguendus* now only found in Northern Scotland. The male might possibly also be confused with that of the light form of *B. campestris*, which however has the characteristics of subgenus *Psithyrus*.

Autecology

This species did occur in open flower rich grassland; in Scotland it is found in the Machair habitat. Queens emerge from hibernation from May onwards. They are underground nesters and will nest in disused mammal holes, even rabbit holes and form pocket maker colonies. The colony cycle is for between 3-4 months and this species will have one colony cycle per year. It has small colony size with under 75 workers and is a long-tongued species, particularly associated with red clover and other legumes. Males will 'nest entrance gather' around the outside of a nest trying to enter to mate with the queens or patrol around the entrance scent marking.

Predators and parasites

There are no recorded predators or parasites of this species.

THE BUMBLEBEES OF KENT

♀ *Bombus distinguendus*—Great yellow bumblebee © Dave Goulson

Face-on view of a queen *Bombus subterraneus* Short-haired bumblebee (left) and worker
B. ruderatus Ruderal bumblebee— from pinned specimens in the NHM collection
© Nick Withers

CHAPTER 4   SUBGENUS AND SPECIES PROFILES

♂ *Bombus subterraneus*—Short-haired bumblebee, photographed in New Zealand
© Nikki Gammans

♀ *Bombus subterraneus*—Short-haired bumblebee, photographed in New Zealand
© Nikki Gammans

♀ *Bombus subterraneus*—Short-haired
bumblebee © Nikki Gammans

THE BUMBLEBEES OF KENT

Bombus subterraneus (Linnaeus, 1758) Short-haired Bumblebee

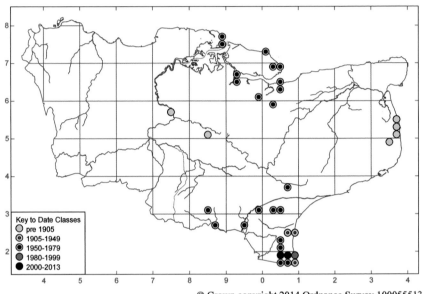

© Crown copyright 2014 Ordnance Survey 100055513

Distribution and Statuses

This bee was once fairly frequent in the county, which was its stronghold in the UK. It was last found in Britain at Dungeness, in 1988, and declared extinct in year 2000.

Nationally, this was a local but widespread species in the south until its catastrophic decline in the 1960s and 70s.

Kent status: Extinct.   National status: UK BAP Priority Species.

IUCN Statuses: Kent Extinct (RE); UK Extinct (RE).

CHAPTER 4   SUBGENUS AND SPECIES PROFILES

Identification and similar species
This bee is a black short-haired species with yellow banding on the front and rear of the thorax and two or three narrow yellow bands on the gaster, the last close to the white tail. The second thoracic band is always narrower than the first. This is the only true bumblebee species in the UK to have yellow hairs next to the white tail. Dark forms may be totally black apart from a dark chocolate-coloured tail. The male appears very different, being extensively yellow over the abdomen and thorax with a black band of hairs between the wing bases.

The female castes of this bumble have the giz of an intermediate form of *Bombus ruderatus.* However in *B. subterraneus* the second band of the thorax is narrower than the first, whilst in *B. ruderatus* they are the same width. *B. subterraneus* also does not have ginger hairs around the mandibles and has a shorter face.

Autecology
It is found foraging on open flower rich habitats. Queens were noted to appear in the UK May-June but in continental Europe they can emerge from late April onwards. *Bombus subterraneus* nests in disused rodent holes. Colonies live for 3-4 months and have 75-100 workers. It has one colony cycle per year and is a long-tongued species, feeding on red clover, bramble, white dead nettle and comfrey. Males will 'nest entrance gather', scent marking on grass stems and flying in repeated cycles around the nest entrance. Some may also try to enter the nest to mate with a queen.

Predators and parasites
Quarantine work on Swedish queens of this bee has shown a number of endoparasites including microorganisms and the braconid wasp *Syntretus* sp. It is possible that *Bombus barbutellus* was an occasional cuckoo.

THE BUMBLEBEES OF KENT

Subgenus *Thoracobombus* Dalla Torre, 1880
or the *Bombus sylvarum* species group

This subgenus, as currently defined, was formed from the unification of nine former subgenera and contains 50 world species, making it the second largest in *Bombus*. It is Nearctic, Neotropical, Palaearctic and Oriental in geographical distribution.

Members of this subgenus are variable in size and colour, including the medium-sized British forms and the largest *Bombus* species, the south American *B. dahlbomii*.

The British species are *Bombus humilis, B. muscorum, B. pascuorum, B. pomorum, B. ruderarius* and *B. sylvarum*. *B. pomorum* was once assigned to the synonymised subgenus *Rhodobombus*. The remaining British species are known as carder bees from their habit of nesting in grass tussocks, weaving the contained dead grass blades into a thatching over the nest.

Bombus pomorum is only tentatively placed on the British list; it could either be a species which attempted and failed colonisation or an example of a very early extinction in Britain. It has not been recorded here since 1854.

These are fairly long-tongued bumbles of which three are late emergers, *Bombus humilis, B. muscorum* and *B. sylvarum*. The first two of these species are difficult to distinguish in the field, the main character used being the presence or absence of a few black hairs near the wing bases. *B. pascuorum* and *B. ruderarius* are early emergers. The latter has declined, whilst the former remains one of the county's most common bumblebees.

The species are pocket makers.

CHAPTER 4   SUBGENUS AND SPECIES PROFILES

♀ *Bombus humilis*—Brown-banded carder bee © Nikki Gammans

♂ *Bombus humilis*—Brown-banded carder bee © Steve Falk

Bombus humilis Illiger, 1806   Brown-banded Carder Bee

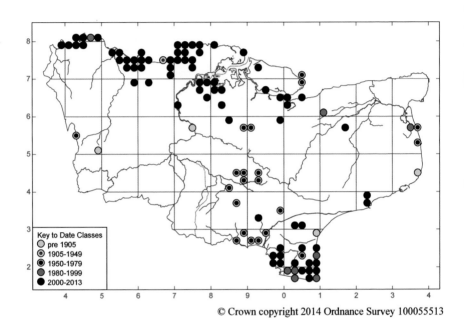

© Crown copyright 2014 Ordnance Survey 100055513

Distribution and Statuses

This carder bee is found mainly in coastal areas, such as grazing marsh. It was formerly more widespread before its retreat to the coast and is now scarce in the county.

Nationally, this is a declining southern species. Agri-environment schemes may bring it a reprieve.

Kent status: Scarce B.   National status: UK BAP Priority Species.

IUCN statuses: Kent Vulnerable (VU); UK Vulnerable (VU).

CHAPTER 4   SUBGENUS AND SPECIES PROFILES

Identification and similar species
This bee bears a strong resemblance to the closely related *Bombus muscorum*. It has a bright reddish brown top to the thorax and yellowish hairs on the sides of the thorax and on the gaster. Unlike *B. muscorum*, it has a brown band of hairs on T2 but this is not always prominent. In almost all examples, there are a few black hairs above the wing bases.

Bombus humilis differs from *B. pascuorum*, another closely related species, in having no black hairs on the gaster.

Autecology
It is found in open grassland meadows and heathland. Queens emerge from hibernation May onwards. As with all carder bees they nest on the ground surface in long tussock grass. It will nest in drier areas than *Bombus muscorum*. The colonies live for 3-4 months and there is just one colony cycle per year. It is a pocket maker species and has a fairly long tongue. It forages on tufted vetch, white dead nettle, red clover and birds foot trefoil amongst others.

Predators and parasites
A host of the parasitic bumblebee *Bombus campestris*.

Bombus muscorum (Linnaeus, 1758)   **Moss Carder Bee**

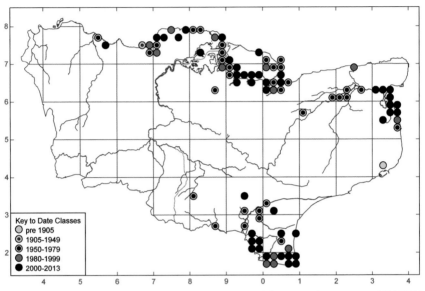

© Crown copyright 2014 Ordnance Survey 100055513

Distribution and Statuses

This carder bee is scarce and also retreating to the coast, although it was never as frequent inland as the previous species. It is possibly still declining in coastal habitats although agri-environment schemes may bring it a reprieve.

This bee is widespread but mainly coastal nationally, and showing a decline.

Kent status: Scarce A.   National status: UK BAP Priority Species.

IUCN statuses: Kent Vulnerable (VU); UK Vulnerable (VU).

Identification and similar species
This bee has a brightly coloured reddish brown top to the thorax and yellow hairs on the sides and on the gaster. It differs from *Bombus humilis* in lacking the brown abdominal band on T2 and has no black hairs near the wing bases. There are no black hairs on the gaster, unlike the similar *B. pascuorum*.

Autecology
This bee is found on coastal marshes and flower rich grasslands. Queens emerge from hibernation May onwards and will live for 3-4 months. They have one colony cycle and nest on the ground in long tussock grass surfaces as all carders do, often in slightly wetter habitats than *Bombus humilis* (which often co-occurs in Kent). Colonies can be defensive when disturbed. They are pocket makers and the colony size is small, between 50-120 workers. It is a fairly long tongue length bee which will forage on red clover, tufted vetch, white dead nettle amongst other legumes.

Predators and parasites
This species may be a host of *Bombus campestris*.

THE BUMBLEBEES OF KENT

♀ *Bombus muscorum*—Moss carder bee © Jeremy Early

♂ *Bombus muscorum*—Moss carder bee © Nick Withers

CHAPTER 4   SUBGENUS AND SPECIES PROFILES

Worker *Bombus pascuorum*—
Common carder bee © Dave Goulson

♂ *Bombus pascuorum*—Common carder bee © Steve Falk

THE BUMBLEBEES OF KENT

Bombus pascuorum (Scopoli, 1763)   **Common Carder Bee**

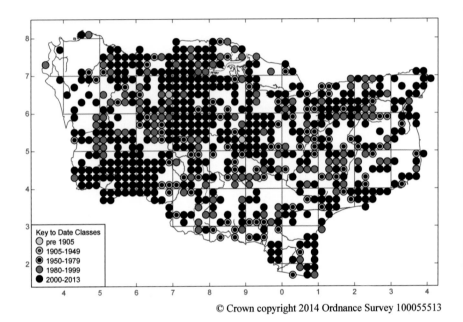

Key to Date Classes
- ○ pre 1905
- ◉ 1905-1949
- ◉ 1950-1979
- ◉ 1980-1999
- ● 2000-2013

© Crown copyright 2014 Ordnance Survey 100055513

Distribution and Statuses
This is a common and widely distributed species in the county, not showing any signs of decline.

It is distributed nationally from Cornwall to Kent and north to the Orkneys.

IUCN statuses: Kent Least Concern (LC); UK Least Concern (LC).

Identification and similar species
This species is highly variable in colour, which is to some extent geographically based. Northern specimens tend to be much lighter than those from the south. It has a ginger thorax with blonde sides, and with

134

some black hairs interspersed in the ginger throughout the top of the thorax. The abdomen is particularly variable, often ginger with black hairs particularly on the sides of T3, T4 and T5. Sometimes the whole base of the abdomen, T1 to T3, is black haired.

There are always some black hairs on the abdomen of this species whilst in *Bombus humilis* and *B. muscorum* these are not present. Sometimes this species has been confused with *B. hypnorum*, which has a white tail as opposed to the ginger of *B. pascuorum*.

Autecology
This species is found in a wide variety of habitats including flower rich grasslands and gardens. Queens emerge from March onwards. It is the only common species of carder bee. It is a ground surface nester in long grass and a pocket maker. This species has a longer colony cycle of 4-5 months and colony size may be as many as 150 workers. It has one colony cycle per year. *Bombus pascuorum* is a long-tongued species and will forage on many different flowers including common garden species such as lavender, foxgloves, comfrey and white dead nettle.

Predators and parasites
Bombus pascuorum is a confirmed host of the cuckoo *B. campestris*. The braconid wasp *Syntretus splendidus* has been reared from queens of *B. pascuorum*.

Bombus pomorum (Panzer, 1801)   **Apple Bumblebee**

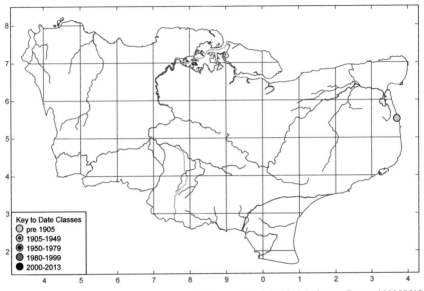

© Crown copyright 2014 Ordnance Survey 100055513

Distribution and Statuses
It is unclear if this ever was a true British species, having only been recorded in Britain from Deal Sandhills in the 1830s and 1854. It may have been an unsuccessful attempt at colonisation or an early extinction (Falk, 1991).

Kent status: Extinct.

IUCN Statuses: Kent Extinct (RE); UK Extinct (RE).

Identification and similar species
This bee generally resembles *Bombus ruderarius* but with more red on the gaster. Given the unlikely event of it being recorded in Kent again, no detailed comparison with other species needs to be given.

CHAPTER 4   SUBGENUS AND SPECIES PROFILES

Autecology
Habitats found were in sand dunes and marsh. Long-tongued pocket maker species, nesting underground.

Predators and parasites
There were no known cuckoos on this species in the UK. In continental Europe *Bombus campestris* is a parasite.

Pinned ♀ *Bombus pomorum*—Apple bumblebee, from the NHM collection © Nick Withers

Pinned ♀ *Bombus pomorum*—Apple bumblebee, from the NHM collection © Nick Withers

THE BUMBLEBEES OF KENT

Bombus ruderarius (Müller, 1776)   Red-shanked Carder Bee

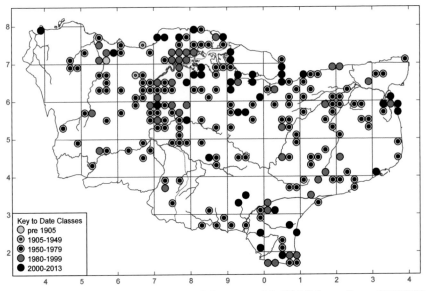

Distribution and Statuses
This was formerly a widespread, frequent species in the county but declined significantly in the 1960s and 70s. It is now scarce in Kent.

It has also declined nationally.

Kent status: Rare.   National status: UK BAP Priority Species.

IUCN statuses: Kent Vulnerable (VU); UK Endangered (EN).

Identification and similar species
This is a medium sized, black haired bee with a ginger-red tail in the female castes, whilst the male is similar but with a greyish-yellow collar on the front of the thorax and back of the thorax. The corbicular hairs are red in this species.

CHAPTER 4   SUBGENUS AND SPECIES PROFILES

Bombus ruderarius is superficially similar to *B. lapidarius*, but is a smaller species and the female castes have the red corbicular hairs on the hind legs compared to the black of *B. lapidarius*. The male of *B. ruderarius* also lacks the yellow tuft of hairs on the face present in male *B. lapidarius*.

The males could potentially be confused with male *Bombus rupestris* as they also have greyish-yellow bands on the thorax but these often also appear on the abdomen. The latter also have the characteristics of the cuckoos.

Autecology
It is found in a variety of habitats including flower rich grasslands and woodland edges. Queens emerge from April onwards. They are pocket makers and surface nesters in long tussock grass. Colonies live for 3-4 months, have a maximum of 100 workers and there is one colony cycle per year. They will forage on white clover and bramble amongst others. Males will form a 'male patrol group' along hedges and shrubs of suitable flowers, patrolling up and down waiting for the queens to emerge.

Predators and parasites
This bee is a host of *B. campestris*.

♂ *Bombus ruderarius*—Red-shanked carder bee
© Nikki Gammans

♀ *Bombus ruderarius*—
Red-shanked carder bee © Steve Falk

139

Bombus sylvarum (Linnaeus, 1761)   **Shrill Carder Bee**

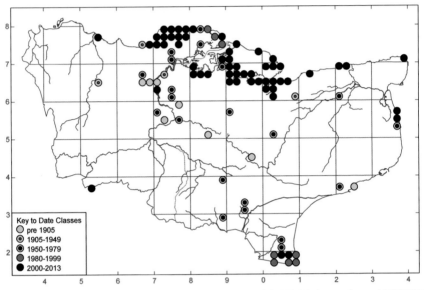

© Crown copyright 2014 Ordnance Survey 100055513

Distribution and Statuses

This was once a widespread, southern species, although most Kent data are from the coast. Although still recorded on the north Kent marshes, it has declined inland.

There has been a severe national decline in this species, the Thames Gateway being one of its last strongholds.

Kent status: Rare.   National status: UK BAP Priority Species.

IUCN statuses: Kent Vulnerable (VU); UK Endangered (EN).

Identification and similar species

Although sometimes called non-descript, with a little experience this is a distinctive species. The females castes and male are similar in colouration. The bee is of medium size with greyish-yellow bands on the front and rear of the thorax and extensively on the abdomen. There is a black stripe between the wing bases and the tail is reddish. There are no similarly coloured bumbles in the UK. A field character useful in identification is the higher pitched buzz than in other bumblebees.

A dark form of this species is of occasional occurrence in the county, resembling *Bombus ruderarius* although more unkempt. Also on the underside of this form there are greyish-yellow hairs on the bases of the legs which are not present in *B. ruderarius*.

Autecology
Bombus sylvarum can be found in a variety of habitats including flower rich grasslands and heathland. Queens emerge from hibernation in May onwards. A surface nesting bumblebee like all carder bees. With a colony cycle of 4-5 months, new queens and males not emerging until September. A small species with a mid length tongue and is a pocket maker. Small colony size of under 100 workers and one colony cycle per year. Forages on black horehound, birds foot trefoil, white dead nettle and other legumes.

Predators and parasites
It is possible that this bee is a host of *Bombus campestris*.

THE BUMBLEBEES OF KENT

♂ *Bombus sylvarum*—Shrill carder bee © Nick Withers

Worker *Bombus sylvarum*—Shrill carder bee © Jeremy Early

CHAPTER 5
WHERE TO GO NEXT

Further reading, identification and field studies

If you have been encouraged, even inspired by the pages of this book you may wish to go further to expand on your knowledge. The three avenues in the heading often go together and to undertake one, some activity in the others may be necessary.

Under further reading, the main works on the British bumblebees are that of Sladen (1912), Alford (1975) and Benton (2006). These give a good account of biology and identification. There are two less technical books which will be found useful to identify British bumblebees, Prŷs-Jones and Corbet (2011) and Edwards and Jenner (2009). It is advised when specialising in one invertebrate group to purchase an identification book specifically for that group as general identification guides to invertebrates will not cover all species. With over 10,000 UK invertebrate species it would be impossible for one book to cover all for identification.

To find out more about a species of bumblebee in your garden or the local park, identification is always the first step. "Googling" your species name may give instant access to web pages describing the habits and geographical distribution of the insect. Local bumblebee faunas have been written for several counties and a region.

To advance in bee identification it may be necessary to take specimens – of course this may put off some people. It may be possible to visit local museums which have a good insect collection and a knowledgeable curator such as Tunbridge Wells museum (Dr Ian Beavis) who can assist you with pinned specimens and identification. The next issue is finding a reliable, scientific key; and here is the first obstacle. For most insect groups, the Royal Entomological Society has published excellent handbooks for the identification of the British species. The aculeates are all covered, apart from the bees, where a handbook is in preparation. The bumblebee key in Benton (2006) is reliable and based largely on the colour characters of the hair although these can sun-bleach and abrade with the increasing age of the bee. A good digital image of a bumblebee will often allow its identification by an expert but this may not always be possible if vital characteristics are not shown.

If you want to learn more about the behaviour, biology and population dynamics of the world's social bees, wasps and ants, the books by Edward Wilson are highly recommended, e.g. the Insect Societies (1971). The bees were the subject of a world generic revision by Michener (2007), which briefly covers the biology where known of all the bee genera, each under their heading. There are also several very readable accounts of bee behaviour, in less technical works.

When one comes to field studies, there are many areas where scientific work can usefully be done. Population studies are vital for conservation work. It has already been mentioned that bumblebee nests are difficult to locate and hence true abundance hard to ascertain. A good method for finding the nests would revolutionise our knowledge. It is true that repeated recording of a local species at one site indicates a certain level of abundance. If a species is really scarce, it may not always be recorded, even when searched for at a known site. Another indirect measure of abundance is in the number of grid squares from where a species is recorded. This is strictly geographical distribution but as with repeated recording at a site, it indirectly shows how common a species is.

To gain good field knowledge of our species of bumblebee, various locations in different habitats will need to be visited. Many of these locations are ecologically sensitive sites and nature reserves, owned and/or managed by conservation bodies such as the county Wildlife Trusts, the RSPB, National Trust and the Woodland Trust, or are in private ownership, for example golf courses and sand pits. A permit must be first obtained to record in such areas. The warden (manager or ranger) of such a reserve may wish to direct you away from areas that are sensitive to trampling or other disturbance. It is good practice once you have completed your sampling to give the species list recorded to the site manager. Some reserves may have strict rules about destructive sampling i.e. taking specimens to kill and pin for identification purposes.

If getting started in biodiversity recording is daunting, there are clubs and societies with experienced members who are often willing to help. If you live in Kent, there is the Kent Field Club, the natural history society of the county, with members who collectively have extensive knowledge in just about every taxon group one can think of. The Club holds field meetings nearly every weekend during the spring, summer and early autumn months and beginners are welcome. The Kent and Medway Biological Records Centre is always interested in obtaining reliable data to ensure that potential impact on surrounding biodiversity is properly assessed during planning and development, and to assist with education, research and other conservation works and projects. The BRC staff are always helpful in promoting an understanding of biological recording. They may also be interested in time you can volunteer. If you just like getting out and getting hands on to help to conserve nature, then you might like to volunteer for the Kent Wildlife Trust. Kent is well served by these organisations and indeed a number of other local recording groups who all pull together to conserve and protect our sensitive wildlife. If you are looking for specialist advice regarding any taxonomic group then any of the three organisations mentioned above will be able to assist or direct you to the best source of help and advice if more specialist knowledge is required. The Short-haired bumblebee reintroduction project also looks for volunteers with good bumblebee and wild flower identification skills, and the Bumblebee Conservation Trust looks for volunteers to complete Beewalks across the country. Please see their website on how to get involved: **http://bumblebeeconservation.org/**

The UK Bees, Wasps and Ants Recording Society (BWARS) has members with a wealth of knowledge in all aspects of aculeate biology and taxonomy. BWARS often runs workshops in the winter months to help beginners identify pinned aculeates of difficult groups. Their two day autumn meeting is an annual gathering and a forum for amateurs to rub shoulders with the most knowledgeable aculeate biologists in the country, as well as participate in identification workshops. The BWARS web pages have excellent photographs covering the vast majority of the British aculeates under their species heads.

Research

In reading this book you can see there is still a lot missing in our bumblebee knowledge, such as effects of disease and parasites on populations, the impact of pesticides and where bumblebees choose to nest. More detailed knowledge and funding is required to aid their conservation.

Of the bees, honeybees are the best studied due to their production of honey and the knowledge from honeybee keepers. They are thought traditionally and incorrectly to be the most economically important of the bees. In comparison information on solitary bees is severely lacking; with some 230 species in the UK and few being studied, urgent ecological research is needed to aid their conservation.

It is hoped reading this book may inspire some of our next generation of scientists to investigate these questions.

REFERENCES AND RECOMMENDED READING

References

Alford, D.V. (1975). *Bumblebees.* Davis-Poynter.

Allen, G.W. (2009). *The Bees, Wasps and Ants of Kent.* Kent Field Club.

Baldock, D.W. (2008). *The Bees of Surrey.* Surrey Wildlife Trust.

Benton, T. (2006). *Bumblebees.* Harper Collins.

Brook, J. and Brook, G (2009). *The Dragonflies of Kent.* Kent Field Club.

Edwards, M. and Jenner, M. (2009). *Field Guide to the Bumblebees of Great Britain & Ireland.* Ocelli Limited.

Falk, S.J. (1991). *A review of the scarce and threatened bees, wasps and ants of Great Britain.* Nature Conservancy Council (Now Natural England).

Gauld, I. and Bolton, B. (1996). *The Hymenoptera.* The Natural History Museum, London. Reprinted by Oxford University Press.

Michener, C.D. (2007). *The Bees of the World.* Johns Hopkins University Press.

Prŷs-Jones, O.E. and Corbet, S.A. (2011). *Bumblebees* (Naturalist series). Pelagic Publishing.

Richards, O.W. (1968). The subgeneric divisions of the genus *Bombus* Latreille. *Bulletin of the British Museum (Natural History), Entomology* 22: 211-276.

Shirt, D.B. (Ed.) (1987). *British Red Data Books: 2 Insects.* Nature Conservancy Council.

Sladen, F.W.L. (1912). *The humble bee: its life history and how to domesticate it.* Macmillan and Co., London.

van Achterberg, C. and Haeselbarth, E. (2003). Revision of the genus *Syntretus* Foerster (Hymenoptera: Braconidae: Euphorinae) from Europe. *Zool. Med. Leiden* 77: 9-78

Waite, A. (2000). *The Kent Red Data Book.* Kent County Council.

Williams, P.H. (1991). The bumble bees of the Kashmir Himalaya (Hymenoptera: Apidae, Bombini). *Bulletin of the British Museum (Natural History), Entomology,* 60 (1):1-204.

Williams, P.H. (2000). Some properties of rarity scores used in site quality assessment. *British Journal of Entomology and Natural History*, 13. 73-86.

Williams, P.H. (2008). Do the parasitic *Psithyrus* resemble their host bumblebees in colour pattern? *Apidologie* 39 (2008) 637-649.

Williams, P.H., Cameron, S.A., Hines, H.M., Cederberg, B. and Rasmont, P. (2008). A simplified subgeneric classification of the bumblebees (genus *Bombus*). *Apidologie* 39 (2008) 1-29.

Williams, P.H., Thorp, R.W., Richardson, L.L. and Colla, S.R. (2014). *Bumble Bees of North America. An identification guide.* Princeton University Press.

Wilson, E.O. (1971). *The Insect Societies.* Cambridge Mass.: Harvard University Press.

REFERENCES AND FURTHER READING

Recommended Further Reading

Books

Goulson, D. (2010). *Bumblebees; their behaviour, ecology and conservation.* Oxford University Press, Oxford.

Kirk, W.D.J. and Howes, F.N. (2012). *Plants for bees.* IBRA.

Pinchen, B.J. (2004). *A pocket guide to the bumblebees of Britain and Ireland.* Lymington: Forficula Books.

Websites

Dr Paul Williams bumblebee expert at the Natural History Museum
http://www.nhm.ac.uk/bombus

IUCN bumblebee specialist group
http://www.iucn.org/bumblebees

Royal Entomological Society
http://www.royensoc.co.uk/

Bees, Wasps and Ants Recording Society
http://www.bwars.com/

Bumblebee Conservation Trust: everything you need to know about bumblebees
http://bumblebeeconservation.org/

Natural England: advice and guidance on agri-environment schemes
http://www.naturalengland.org.uk/

THE BUMBLEBEES OF KENT

RSPB: discusses habitat creation across on their reserves across the UK
http://www.rspb.org.uk/

Hymettus: autecology research on bees, wasps and ants
http://www.hymettus.org.uk/

Entomological Suppliers

Watkins and Doncaster, PO box 5, Cranbrook, Kent, TN18 5EZ. T. 01580 753133 **www.watdon.com**

EH Thorne (Beehives) Ltd, Beehive Business Park, Rand, Nr Wragby, Market Rasen, LN8 5NJ   T. 01673 858555 **www.thorne.co.uk**

Key papers

Biesmeijer, J.C., Roberts, S.P., Reemer, M., Ohlemueller, R., Edwards, M., Peeters, T., Schaffers, A., Potts, S.G., Kleukers, R., Thomas, C.D., Settele, J. & Kunin, W.E. (2006). Parallel declines in pollinators and insect-pollinated plants in Britain and the Netherlands. *Science* 313: 351-354

Blake, R.J., Woodcock, B.A., Westbury, D.B., Sutton, P. and Potts, S.G. (2011). Enhancing habitat to help the plight of the bumblebee. *Pest Management Science* 67: 377-379

Brown, M. J. F. (2011). Conservation. The trouble with bumblebees. *Nature*, Vol. 469, No. 7329, p. 169-170.

Brown, M. J. F. and Paxton, R. J. (2009). The conservation of bees: a global perspective. *Apidologie*, Vol. 40, No. 3, p. 410-416.

REFERENCES AND FURTHER READING

Carvell, C., Roy, D.B., Smart, S.M., Pywell, R.F., Preston, C.D. and Goulson, D. (2006). Declines in forage availability for bumblebees at a national scale. *Biological Conservation* 132, 481-489

Edwards, M. and Williams, P.H. (2004). Where have all the bumblebees gone, and could they ever return? *British Wildlife* 15: 305-312

Gammans, N., Edwards, M., and Banks, B. (2009). The return of the native: loss and repatriation of the Short-haired Bumblebee *Bombus subterraneus*. *British Wildlife* **21: 2**

Goulson, D., Lye, G.C., and Darvill, B. (2008). Decline and conservation of bumblebees. *Annual Review of Entomology* 53: 191-208

Goulson, D. (2006). The demise of the bumblebee in Britain. *The Biologist* 53: 294-299

Goulson, D., Rayner, P., Dawson, B. & Darvill, B. (2011). Translating research into action; bumblebee conservation as a case study. *Journal of Applied Ecology* 48: 3-8

Potts S.G., Biesmeijer J.C., Kremen C., Neumann P., Schweiger O., and Kunin W.E. (2010). Global pollinator declines: trends, impacts and drivers. *Trends in Ecology and Evolution* 25: 345-353

Williams, P.H. (1982). The distribution and decline of British bumble bees (*Bombus* Latr.). *Journal of Apicultural Research* 21: 236-245.

Williams, P.H. (1986). Environmental change and the distributions of British bumble bees (*Bombus* Latr.). *Bee World* 67: 50-61.

Williams, P.H. (1988). Habitat use by bumble bees (*Bombus* spp.). *Eco-*

THE BUMBLEBEES OF KENT

logical Entomology 13: 223-237

Williams, P.H. (1989). Why are there so many species of bumble bees at Dungeness? *Botanical Journal of the Linnaean Society* 101: 31-44.

Williams, P.H., and Osborne, J.L. (2009). Bumblebee vulnerability and conservation world-wide. *Apidologie* 40: 367-387.

GLOSSARY

Abdomen or gaster- The third and last segment of an insect's body.

Aculeates- The stinging Hymenoptera.

Angiosperms- The flowering plants.

Antenna- One of a pair of simple sensory feelers, jointed to the face of the insect.

Association- In ecology, where two different species spend at least part of their life cycle bound together in a symbiosis e.g. commensalism.

Autecology (or species ecology)- The behaviours of the individual species and how it interacts with its environment.

BAP (Biodiversity Action Plan)- program recognised internationally for protecting threatened species or habitats.

Batesian mimicry- A harmless species imitates a harmful species as a predator defence.

Big 7 bumblebee species- Refers to our most common bumblebee species in the UK; buff-tailed, red-tailed, white-tailed, garden, early, common carder and the tree bumblebee.

Bumblebee- With queen and worker caste. Queen starts colony and forages until first brood (only workers) emerges. Female workers then forage and feed brood.

Caste- Social division of role of individual within a colony.

Chitin- The exoskeleton of insects, which is indigestible to many species.

Commensal- an organism which spends all or part of its life cycle with a host of a different species – the commensal benefits but the host is unharmed – if both benefit then this is "mutualism".

Corbicula (or pollen basket)- On female hind legs, used to hold pollen for transport to nest.

Cuckoo bumblebee- Male or female parasite of a social or 'true' bumblebee colony.

THE BUMBLEBEES OF KENT

Diploid- Heterozygote- All females have double the number of chromosomes as males (i.e. females have paired chromosomes).

Drone- Male honeybee.

Early emergers- Queens which emerge from hibernation from January-April.

Egg- Organic vessel in which the embryo first begins to develop; laid by a female and soon hatches into the larva. The first stage of metamorphosis.

Endoparasite- An organism which develops inside another. The parasite benefits; the host's fitness is reduced but it is not killed.

Endoparasitoid- An organism which develops inside another, the host, feeding on it and eventually killing it.

Eusocial- Social colony of related individuals with queens being the only reproductives.

Exoskeleton- the hard outside shell of an insect, spider, mite or crustacean, to which the internal muscles are attached. The shell is formed of plates or sclerites, in insects made of chitin.

Foraging- the act of going to search for food.

Haploid- Hemizygote- All males have half the number of chromosomes as females (i.e. males have unpaired chromosomes).

Hibernation (diapause)- Used by species in unfavourable weather conditions i.e. winter. In bumblebees it is only the new queens which enter hibernation.

Honeybee- Advanced eusocial bee (with queen and worker caste) of the genus *Apis*. Queen does not forage for the colony and lacks pollen baskets. Female workers forage for the colony and feed the brood.

Hymenoptera- Order of insects which contain the ants, bees, wasps, ichneumons and sawflies.

Indigenous- Native to the country in question.

Inquiline- A permanent social parasite, one without a worker caste e.g. cuckoo bumblebees.

Late emergers- Queens which emerge from hibernation May onwards.

Larva- Juvenile stage, metamorphoses into the pupa; the feeding, growing stage. The second stage of metamorphosis.

Male group patrolling- Males will fly together in groups along hedgerows or shrubs patrolling for virgin queens.

Mandibles- appendages close to the insect's mouth. Their function is to cut, bite, grasp food and/or to use in defence or attack.

Metamorphosis- Distinctly different stages in the life span of an insect e.g. egg, larva, pupa, adult – this is four stage metamorphosis.

Monogynous- One queen per colony.

Mullerian mimicry- Poisonous or harmful species mimic each other as warning signals to predators.

Nectar- Sugar rich liquid produced by plants.

Nest entrance gather- Males congregate around nest entrance holes waiting for the virgin queens to emerge.

Ovipositor- Organ used to lay eggs in females.

Parasite- An organism which lives at the expense of another, the host. The parasite does not directly kill its host.

Parasitoid- A parasitic organism which kills its host.

Pheromone- is a secreted 'scent', an external hormone that triggers a response in members of the same species.

Pocket makers- Nesting type of mainly long-tongued bumblebees which create pockets of pollen at the base of the brood-cell clump that the larvae feed themselves from.

Pollen- haploid male gametes (genetic material).

Pollen storers- Nesting type of mainly short-tongued bumblebees where pollen in stored in wax cells and fed individually to the larvae.

Pollination- The process of male gametes (pollen) being transferred from the anther (the male part of the plant) to the stigma (the female part of the plant). This occurs in angiosperms (the flowering plants).

Polygynous- Many queens per colony.

Pupa- Follows the larval stage; after pupal stage the adults emerge. The third stage of metamorphosis.

Queen- Egg-laying matriarch of the colony. Can lay both female and male eggs.

Royal Jelly ("Brood food")- Is secreted by honeybee workers and fed to all caste larvae. Worker larvae are fed pollen after three days, for a new queen only royal jelly is given to feed the larva.

Sclerites- the "plates" made of chitin which form an insect's exoskeleton.

Sexuals- Males and reproductive females.

Solitary bee - Only female and males, no worker caste and no colony is formed.

Sonication (buzz pollination)- A bumblebee dislocates its wing muscles and vibrates its body dislodging pollen held tightly on a plant's anther.

Sternum (*pl.* Sterna)- A lower sclerite or plate of the abdomen.

Sting- a sharp organ that delivers venom, evolutionarily derived from the egg-laying apparatus of the female.

Stingless bees- Advanced eusocial bees of the tribe Meliponini, almost entirely tropical in distribution.

Subgenus (*pl.* Subgenera)- A taxonomic rank below genus and above species.

Swarming- The old queen honeybee plus half of the workers leave the hive to start a new colony.

Tagma (*pl.* Tagmata)- Three parts of insect body; head, thorax and abdomen.

Tergum (*pl.* Terga)- An upper sclerite or plate of the abdomen. Female bees have six terga and males seven.

Thorax- The middle part of an insect's body where wings and legs are attached.

Tibia (*pl.* Tibiae)- The joint of the female bee's hind leg which has the pollen basket.

'True' bumblebee- Social bumblebee as opposed to a cuckoo bumblebee parasite.

Wax- secreted by female worker and queen bumblebees and honeybees from wax-producing mirror glands on the inner sternites. Used by bees to store pollen and nectar and for brood development i.e. eggs laid inside.

Workers- Females whose role within the nest is to tend the queen, incubate eggs and feed larvae, and to forage for the colony; they are unmated but can lay male eggs under certain circumstances.

ACKNOWLEDGEMENTS

We thank the committee and members of BWARS, (the UK Bees, Wasps and Ants Recording Society) for access to their data holdings. Also, thanks are due to the manager, Dr Hannah Cook, and staff of the Kent & Medway Biological Records Centre (KMBRC) for giving us access to their general database of Kent *Bombus* and to the dataset of the late E.G. Philp. A full list of Kent *Bombus* observers whose records are used, is given below.

The various maps used in this book were prepared using the computer program DMAP for Windows written by Dr A.J. Morton.

Thanks are due to Jeremy Early, Steve Falk, Dave Goulson, Louise Hislop, Alan Kenworthy, Duncan Lawie, Peter Maton, John Oates, Nick Owen, Sarah Seymour, Andy Tebbs, Siew Lee Vorley, Gill Williams and Nick Withers for permission to use their photographs in the book. Some of Nikki Gammans' own photographs are also used. Credits are given with the photographs.

We also thank Tony Hopkins for permission to use his well-known bumblebee life cycle diagram in the book. The Bumblebee Conservation Trust are thanked for permission to use one of their diagrams. Dave Goulson gave permission to use his bumblebee hind legs diagram. The eight whole insect drawings and two anatomy diagrams were produced by Geoff Allen. Some of the former have appeared in other publications.

A number of people have proof read various draft forms of the book and made useful and invaluable comments. These include Dr Paul Williams, Professor Dave Goulson, Ian Tittley, Richard Moyse, Nick Withers, Simon Springate and Alan Kenworthy. Dr Hannah Cook read an early version of Chapter 5, Where to go next, giving valuable insights into the work of the KMBRC and putting biodiversity recording into the planning and development context. The authors fully accept that any errors which remain are their responsibility.

ACKNOWLEDGEMENTS

The following observers, past and present, have Kent *Bombus* records used in this book. Their contributions vary from one or two records of *B. hypnorum* to extensive datasets covering many species:

K.N. Alexander, J.H. Allchin, G.W. Allen, Pat Allen, Peter Allen, C.H. Andrewes, M. Antoncini, M.E. Archer, S.E.J. Arnold, G. Austen-Price, J.S. Badmin, R. Baker, P. Bance, B.J. Banks, T. Bantock, M. Barnard, M. Barry, E. Bartlett, I.C. Beavis, D. Bennett, J. Bennett, H.J. Berman, F. Booth, C. Borrow, A. Braby, J. Brook, S. Buell, S. Burch, D. Carey, A.E.J. Carter, L. Castro, R. Chapman, D. Cherry, R. Childs, A.J. Chitty, G. Christian, K. Chuter, L. Clemons, W. Clynes, R. Coldbreath, Mr. G.A. Collins, J. Collins, L. Colman, S.U. Connop, H. Cook, H. Cornally, T. Crabb, A. Cragg, A. Craven, R.A. Crowson, S. Crutchley, A. Dabin, A.M. Davidson, J.A. Davidson, C. Davis, J. Davis, Mrs De Pettitt, L. de Sousa, J. Denton, G.H.L. Dicker, M. Dickerson, N. Dickerson, S. Dove, T. Dove, T. Driver, W. Dudley, C.A.W. Duffield, R. Eades, J.P. Early, R. Earwaker, D. Ede, M. Edwards, H. Elgar, J. Ellis, M. Ellison, G.R. Else, J. Elwell, W.A. Ely, M. Enfield, R. Evans, A. Ewing, L. Fail, A. Fairbrass, S.J. Falk, S.F.G. Farmer, J.C. Felton, J. Feltwell, V. Ferman, L. Flower, A. Ford, A. Foster, D. Fothergill, M. Fountain, A. Fray, M. Fray, J.P.H. Frazer, K. Friend, G. Frisby, N. Gammans, D.C. Gardner, D.J. Gibbs, C. Gilmore, A. Golding, R. Gomes, A.S. Grace, D. Grant, J. Green, P. Grilli-Chantler, K.M. Guichard, C. Haes, A.H. Hamm, J. Harris, T. Harris, D. Harvey, P.R. Harvey, G. Hawgood, C. Hayward, G. Hazlehurst, N. Heal, S. Heath, G. Hemington, A. Henderson, G. Hitchcock, P. Hodge, N. Holt, L. Hopkins, D.R. How, I.R. Hudson, S. Hutchin, D. Illsley, T. Ings, A.P. Jarman, M. Jenner, N. Jennings, R.A. Jones, G. Kadas, A. Kenworthy, A. King, W. Kirby, S. Kirk, H. Lamb, P. Larkin, * Latter, D. Lawie, J. Lee, M. Lowe-Wheeler, L. Manning, G. Marchais, L. Marshall, L. Masterman, N. Matthews, S. Matthewson, B. McHale, G. McInnes, M. Meakins, V. Measday, N. Mengham, D. Mills, J. Mitchell, B.D. Moreton, R. Morris,

THE BUMBLEBEES OF KENT

C.H. Mortimer, J. Morton, E. Moss, P. Moss, R.I. Moyse, T. Mullender, R. Nash, J. Nelson, W. Nevard, M. Newcombe, A. Nixon, A. Norman, C. Norman, R. Norman, * Norton, D. Notton, C.V. Nuttman, H. Oehl, * Otley, C. O'Toole, R.E. Oxley, L. Packer, S. Page, R. Parker, A.J. Parr, M. Pavett, N. Pearson, J. Peeling, D. Penney, J. Perry, C. Phillips, E.G. Philp, B.J. Pinchen, J. Pitt, C.W. Plant, M. Playter, R.J. Pollicott, N. Poole, R. Potts, S. Poyser, J. Puckett, H. Pude, R. Purvis, S. Rear, M. Reed, O.W. Richards, G. Ricketts, S.P.M. Roberts, N.A. Robinson, L. Rule, A. Russell-Smith, E. Saunders, S. Saunders, J. Shorter, J. Showers, K.C. Side, H. Silk, F.W.L. Sladen, M.N. Smith, R. Smith, S.D. Smith, U. Smith-Dennis, A. Southern, A. Spalding, R. Spiller, S. Springate, C.J.G. Stanley, A.E. Stubbs, D. Taylor, H. Teare, M. Telfer, P. Thompson, S. Thompson, M. Tilley, M. Tingey, D. Tolput, S. Trangmar, A.M. Tynan, D. Walker, A. Walter, M. Waterhouse, D.M. Watson, A. Watts, C.M. Watts, S. Weeks, J. Weightman, E. Weston, T. Wilkins, D. Wilks, P. Willcocks, P.H. Williams, A. Wilson, P. Wilson, N. Withers, A. Witts, D. Wood, B.E. Woodhams, I.H.H. Yarrow, J. Young.

INDEX to scientific names

[Names in square brackets are not British species]
Page numbers in bold type refer to the main entries for a species whilst italicised numbers refer to photographs or illustrations.

161

THE BUMBLEBEES OF KENT

INDEX to common names

Page numbers in bold type refer to the main entries for a species whilst italicised numbers refer to photographs or illustrations.

THE BUMBLEBEES OF KENT